Medicinal plants of Greece

By GEORGE SFIKAS

Translated by Ellen Sutton

With illustrations in colour by the author

ATHENS

EFSTATHIADIS GROUP S.A.
14, Valtetsiou Str.
106 80 Athens
Tel: (01) 5154650, 6450113
Fax: (01) 5154657
GREECE

ISBN 960 226 076 9

Printed and bound in Greece

CONTENTS

INTRODUCTION

Sailing through the Bay of Patras in a small boat on a March morning, one might imagine oneself to be on a lake in Switzerland. Almost all around the narrow bay rise the mountains of the northern Peloponnese and of Central Greece, up to 2,500 m in height. At that time of year they are still covered with glistening patches of snow. Yet only one month later, in eastern Crete, the spring may already be so far advanced that it has pretty well turned into summer. In the mountains of Macedonia, on the other hand, or in the Pindus range, even August may suddenly bring spells of weather as cold as February, while at the very same time, on the beaches of the Thermaic Gulf and elsewhere in southern Greece, thousands of people are trying to find some relief from the intense summer heat.

This is Greece: a country of contrasts, stretching across the blue waters of the Mediterranean. These differences in climate and topography affect all her living creatures without exception. People, animals, birds and plants are all characterised by a great variability which reflects the considerable differences in climate and topography that gave birth to the unique civilisation of ancient Greece.

This highly variable setting explains why such a small country has 6,000 different species of plant, of which fully one-tenth are unique to Greece. Many of them have marvellous and even exotic flowers and look like precious jewels set against the green velvet of meadows and pastures or the ash grey harshness of rock. However, this book is not concerned with these fantastical embroideries of Nature, but with the humbler, less eye-catching plants of mountains and plains. Among these insignificant species, which are easily passed by unnoticed and carelessly trodden underfoot, are some of the most valuable medicinal plants which for thousands of years have been used to cure human ailments.

It is not by accident that almost all of the pharmaceutical plants or herbs are common and widespread. Only with such species could people have experimented, have compared the effects of specimens after collecting them from different

Peoples throughout the world have used herbs to treat
sickness since time immemorial. Ancient writers and physicians
— Aristotle, Hippocrates, Dioscurides, Theophrastus, Galen, to
mention but a few — have written treatises on the therapeutic
qualities of certain plants and on how to use them, based on the
agreement on their therapeutic properties.

localities and in different seasons, and arrived at a common

Dioscurides medical writings circulated in many copies during the middle ages. The picture above is taken from one of these copies and represents Wisdom proffering the Mandragora plant to the doctor and praising its value. Dioscurides is duly taking notes, while a draughtsman is sketching the specimen.

folk tradition of their time.
The use of herbs continued to be very widespread in Greece,
as in the rest of Europe, during the Middle Ages and in the

subsequent long years of Ottoman rule. The folk doctors, known as *komboyannites* or *Viko doctors* after the valley of Vikos where they gathered their herbs, handed down their prescriptions orally, or occasionally in writing, from generation to generation and from teacher to pupil, often mixing them with magical incantations or Christian prayers to create the suitable psychological atmosphere for the patient to trust in his certain cure.

Since the beginning of the present century, and with the huge strides made by scientific developments generally, herbal therapy has fallen into neglect, and the medicinal ingredients of living plants have to a large extent been replaced by chemical preparations. The last of the folk doctors were discredited as quacks by the increasingly powerful scientific establishment, and many of them died in gaol for their knowledge of the impressive cures that could be wrought by simple preparations from the commonest wild plants. The chemical and pharmaceutical industry and scientific medicine, for whom the *komboyannites* were obnoxious rivals treatening their profits, did all they could to eradicate traditional folk medicine. Their efforts were aided by the fact that there undoubtedly were quack doctors posing as serious physicians, whose useless prescriptions were nothing more than confidence tricks. This played its part in making people lose faith in herbal medicines, and the word *komboyannites* eventually became synonymous with trickster.

However, in more recent years a number of scientists in many different countries have taken a closer look at the plants which were once famed for their therapeutical value. Their studies soon showed that these plants do in fact contain active constituents truly valuable to medicine. Isolating these elements and administering them to patients in natural preparations has proved much more effective than using the equivalent synthetic medication, since the natural form of the active constituent is much more easily assimilated by the human organism.

Today, hundreds of drugs of which the active ingredients are culled from living plants are on sale throughout the world, and there are entire factories devoted solely to the preparation of natural plant essences. To give just a few simple examples: Belladonna *(Atropa belladonna)* provides an effective medicine against Parkinson's disease; Lesser periwinkle *(Vinca minor)*

The famous Vikos Gorge in Epirus, Northern Greece, where the komboyannites or "Vikos doctors" collected their medicinal plants.

contains a depressant; and White false helleborine *(Veratrum album)* is used against hypertension. In neighbouring Bulgaria especially, extensive scientific work is being done on the study of pharmaceutical plants and the production of various highly effective preparations, even though Bulgaria does not have the floral wealth of Greece.

In Greece itself, recognition of the merits of pharmaceutical herbs is still rudimentary, and their exploitation is at the stage where they are not collected so much as plundered like loot by various speculators. As a result, a number of species *(Gentiana lutea, Atropa belladonna. Arctostaphylus uva-ursi,* among others), have already disappeared almost entirely from regions where they once flourished. There is an immediate need for the State to step in and take protective measures, and particularly to forbid the commercial exportation of wild plants. Only properly organised and systematic cultivation of these species can prevent their extinction and conservation laws will have to be promulgated to achieve this.

When I began to write this book, I considered very carefully whether I should give exact locations for the various species, since I did not want to contribute to their disappearance. In the end I decided to leave out any mention of plants which have already become rare, and to list only the more common ones which are not in any danger yet.

This small volume is not, of course, meant to be a complete study of Greek pharmaceutical plants. It relies quite extensively on secondary sources mentioned in the Bibliography, and I have restricted myself to the more reliable and the more thoroughly tested plants. I have deliberately omitted such species as, although undoubtedly possessing valuable medicinal attributes, may cause poisoning when used by the layman, and have limited myself to the better-known harmless species.

I have in each case given the common as well as the Greek and Latin names, a colour photograph or drawing showing the plant in detail, a simple botanical description largely avoiding specialist terms, directions on how the plant should be collected, the ailments against which it is effective, and recipes for its use. The preparations here given are all taken from various books on pharmaceutical herbs (the sources are again acknowledged in the Bibliography). The plants are arranged alphabetically by their most common English name, and a trilingual index (p. 135) is included.

Basic rules to be followed:
For herbal therapy to be properly effective, the following instructions must be observed:

— Remedies must be applied repeatedly and regularly and for an extended period, especially if the illness is a chronic one.

— The plants must be gathered in the proper season as given, and dried as soon as possible after collection by spreading them

11

The medieval herbals illustrated the plants in so stylised a fashion that there was little resemblance to the actual specimen. This was the result of draughtsmen copying one from the other without any knowledge of the living plant. Over the centuries, this meant that its distinguishing characteristics were quite lost.

out well in the shade, unless the sun is specifically indicated. Roots should be washed, and thick roots should always be cut lengthwise before drying.

— Thoroughly dried plants must be stored in a closed glass container in a dry, darkish place.

— No dried plants should be kept for more than two to three years at the most, because they gradually lose their therapeutic effectiveness.

— Care must be taken that the plant being collected or bought is really the one required.

— If after two weeks of using a certain plant remedy it shows no result whatsoever, a different method or a different plant should be tried instead. Not every human organism reacts in exactly the same way.

AND PLEASE
● When you have found the species of plant you wish to gather, do not abuse it by crippling it hopelessly.

● Never uproot the plant unless it is specifically the root you require, and then be particularly careful not to denude the location of all specimens.

● Take only that part of the plant which is needed, and leave some of the flowers for natural re-seeding to repair the damage.

Nature is not inexhaustible. Ruthless collecting of even the most common plant can lead to its extinction.

NOTES ON PREPARING REMEDIES

TEAS or **TISANES** depend for their effectiveness on proper preparation. Whether they are made with cold water only, heated, or actually boiled for a while has a crucial effect on the active constituent of the plant. Unless otherwise stated, it is usually the dried drug that is used, and the teas may be made stronger than here given, depending on individual taste.

Infusions are made by either pouring boiling water on to the plant and allowing the liquid to stand for 10-15 minutes, *OR* by putting plant and water in a covered pan, heating it to boiling point, at once removing from heat and leaving to stand for 10-15 minutes.

Decoctions are made by placing plant in cold water, heating slowly, boiling for 10-15 minutes, and allowing to stand for 15 minutes before straining.

For **POULTICES,** the plants (usually fresh) are bruised with the flat side of a strong knife or ground in a mortar to make a pulp, and applied externally. Sometimes the plant is boiled in a minimum of water.

GREEK NAMES
The correct stress of the Greek names of the plants is indicated by accenting the vowel of the stressed syllable.

COMPLAINTS and REMEDIES

ABDOMINAL SPASMS — Basil
ABSCESSES — Spearmint
  - breast — Parsley
ACNE — Marigold
ADENOPATHY — Cherry
AEROPHAGIA — Celery
AMENORRHEA — Wormwood
AMOEBIA, Intestinal — Pomegranate
ANAEMIA — Blackberry, Elm, Nettle
ANGINA PECTORIS — Elder
ANOREXY — Balm, Juniper
APPETITE, loss of — Balm, Juniper (see also DYS-PEPSIA)

ARTERIOSCLEROSIS — Hawthorn, Onion
ARTHRITIS — Dandelion, Carrot, Celery, Garlic, Lime, Nettle, Walnut, Yarrow

ASTHMA — Coltsfoot
ATONY (lassitude)
  - cardiac — Rosemary
  - general — Cherry, Dandelion, Germander, Juniper, Mulberry, Nettle, Onion, Sage

  - mental — Dandelion
  - nervous — see NEURASTHENIA
  - stomach — Laurel, Sage, Speedwell

BALDING — Lemon, Rosemary, Sage, Walnut

BEE STINGS — Dandelion, Onion
BLADDER
  - disorders of — Ash
  - inflammation — Bearberry, Couchgrass
BLOOD VESSELS
  - cholesterol in — Nettle
  - clotting of — see PHLEBITIS
BOILS — Coltsfoot
BREAST ABSCESS — Parsley

15

BRONCHIAL CATARRH	- Speedwell
BRONCHITIS	- Agrimony, Coltsfoot, Nettle, Marshmallow, Violet
BRUISES	- Agrimony, Comfrey, Marshmallow, Yarrow
BUNIONS	- Walnut
BURNS	- Carrot, Cherry, Comfrey, Onion
CACHEXY	- Agrimony
CANCER of the skin	- Hemlock, Violet
CARBUNCLES	- Coltsfoot, Elder
CARDIAC	
- irregularities	- Hawthorn
- lassitude	- Rosemary
- pains	- Balm
see also HEARTBEAT	
CATARRH	- Mullein, Violet
- bronchial	- Speedwell
- chronic pulmonary	- Agrimony, Elder, Rosemary
CHOLESTEROL	- Lemon, Nettle
CIRRHOSIS of the liver	- Onion
COUGH	- Agrimony, Coltsfoot
COLDS	- Camomile, Lime, Marshmallow, Sage
COLIC	- Agrimony, Spearmint
CONSTIPATION	- Basil, Camomile, Elder
CORNS	- Walnut
CYSTITIS	- Bearberry, Pellitory
DEBILITY	- see ATONY
DERMATITIS, chronic	- Dandelion
DERMATOLOGICAL COMPLAINTS	- Agrimony (see also ACNE, ECZEMA, ITCHING, SKIN, SPOTS)
DIABETIS	- see SUGAR DIABETIS
DIARRHOEA	- Agrimony, Bilberry, Blackberry, Comfrey, Hawthorn, Purple loosestrife, Mullein, Plantain, Strawberry

DIGESTIVE disorders	- Balm, Purple loosestrife, Wormwood
DYSENTERY	- Agrimony, Comfrey, Mullein, Marshmallow, Rosemary
- microbic	- Purple loosestrife
DYSPEPSIA	- Agrimony, Celery, Laurel
- chronic	- Rosemary
DROPSY	- Agrimony, Ash, Parsley, Wormwood
- hepatic	- Dandelion
DUODENAL ULCER	- Comfrey
EARACHE	- Yarrow
ECZEMA	- Elder, Marigold, Purple loose-strife
- chronic	- Dandelion
ENTERITIS	- Bilberry, Marshmallow
ENTEROCOLITIS	- Pear
EPILEPSY	- Valerian
EYES, inflammation of	- Camomile, Speedwell
- septic opthalmitis	- Parsley
EYESIGHT, weak	- Carrot
ERYSIPELAS	- Hemlock, Marigold
FATIGUE, general see also ATONY	- Juniper
FEVER	- Artichoke, Ash, Celery, Vervain, Wormwood
FLATULENCE	- Balm
FRECKLES	- Lime
GALL COMPLAINTS	- Bearberry, Carrot, Couchgrass
GALL STONES	- Bearberry, Couchgrass
GASTRITIS	- Mullein
GENERAL DEBILITY see also ATONY	- Agrimony
GLANDULAR disease see ADENOPATHY	
- misfunctioning	- Dandelion

17

GLYCOSURIA	- Lime
GONORRHEA	- Bearberry
GOUT	- Comfrey, Lime
GUMS, inflamed	- Sage
HAEMATURIA	- Agrimony
HAEMORRHAGES	
- internal	- Purple loosestrife, Shepherd's purse, Yarrow
- kidney	- Strawberry
- menstrual	- Yarrow
HAEMORRHOIDS	- Artichoke, Onion
HAIR, loss of	- Lemon, Rosemary, Sage, Walnut
HEART irregularities	- Rosemary
- fast beating of	- Elm
- pains in	- Balm
HEPATITIC DROPSY	- Dandelion
HEPATITIS, chronic	- Lime
HYPERTENSION	- Ash, Garlic, Mistletoe, Onion, Parsley, Shepherd's purse
HYSTERIA	- Balm, Valerian
INFLAMMATION	
- bladder	- Couchgrass
- eyes	- Camomile, Speedwell
- intestinal lining	- Germander
- kidney	- Couchgrass, Violet
- lungs	- Violet
- mouth	- Bilberry
- skin	- Elder, Marshmallow, Pellitory
- stomach lining	- Germander
- throat	- Bilberry, Sage
- trachea	- Mullein
- urinary tract	- Couchgrass
INFLUENZA	- Elder
INSOMNIA	- Balm, Lemon, Lime, Valerian
INTERNAL HAEMORRHAGE	- Purple loosestrife, Shepherd's purse

INTESTINAL	
- amoebia	- Pomegranate
- inflammation	- Germander
- tapeworm	- Pomegranate, Wormwood
IRRITABILITY	- Balm
ITCHING	- Purple loosestrife
JAUNDICE	- Agrimony
JOINTS, stiffening in	- Artichoke, Celery
KIDNEY	
- disorders	- Ash
- haemorrhage	- Strawberry
- inflammation of	- Agrimony, Bearberry, Couchgrass, Pellitory
- sand	- Parsley
- stones	- Dandelion, Parsley, Stone fern, Wormwood
LACTATION, failing	- Nettle, Vervain
LIVER complaints	- Agrimony, Couchgrass
- cirrhosis of	- Onion
- swollen	- Dandelion
LUMBAGO	- Lime
LUNGS, inflammation of	- Violet
MALARIAL SPLEEN	- Dandelion
MEMORY, failing	- Basil, Sage
MENSTRUATION	
- delayed	- Marigold
- haemorrhage	- Yarrow
- irregular	- Sage
- profuse	- Shepherd's purse
- suppression of	- Wormwood
- too frequent	- Pear
MENTAL FATIGUE	- Dandelion
MICROBIC DYSENTERY	- Purple loosestrife
MIGRAINE	- Agrimony, Basil, Rosemary
MILK failing in nursing mothers	- Nettle, Vervain

MOLES	- Dandelion
MOUTH	
- inflammation of	- Bilberry, Mulberry
- ulcers	- Mulberry
NEPHRITIS	- Agrimony, Pellitory
see also KIDNEY	
NERVOUS irritability	- Balm
- spasms	- Valerian
NEURALGIA	- Camomile, Mullein
NEURASTHENIA	- Globe thistle, Horsemint
NIGHTSWEATS	- Sage
NIPPLES, cracked	- Comfrey
OBESITY	- Camomile, Garlic, Valerian
OPTHALMITIS, septic	- Parsley
PERSPIRATION, excessive	- Sage
PHARYNGITIS	- Agrimony, Marshmallow
PHLEBITIS	- Agrimony, Comfrey
PIMPLES	- Burdock, Dandelion, Speedwell
PSORIASIS	- Hemlock
PULMONARY CATARRH, chronic	- Agrimony, Elder, Rosemary
PYELITIS	- Bearberry
RHEUMATISM	- Agrimony, Carrot, Celery, Couchgrass, Dandelion, Horsemint, Juniper, Lime, Mullein, Nettle, Rosemary, Yarrow
SCIATICA	- Juniper
SCURVY	- Dandelion
SEASICKNESS	- Lemon
SEPTIC WOUNDS	- Agrimony
SHINGLES	- Hemlock, Walnut
SKIN	
- cancer	- Hemlock, Violet
- chronic dermatitis	- Dandelion

- eruptions	- Burdock, Coltsfoot, Dandelion, Speedwell
- flaccid	- Camomile, Sage
- inflammation of	- Elder, Marshmallow, Pellitory
- moles	- Dandelion
- St Anthony's fire, the rose	- Elder, Hemlock, Marigold
- scurvy	- Dandelion
- warts	- Marigold
SLEEPLESSNESS	- Balm, Lemon, Lime, Valerian
SORE THROAT	- Artichoke
SORES	- Ash, Plantain, Purple loose-strife, Rosemary
SPLEEN, complaints of	- Agrimony
- malarial swelling	- Dandelion
SPRAINS	- Agrimony
STIFF JOINTS	- Artichoke, Celery
STINGS	- Onion
STOMACH	
- cramps	- Camomile, Spearmint, Speedwell
- nervous	- Basil
- spasms	- Laurel
- upsets	- Mistletoe, Vervain, Wormwood
SUGAR DIABETIS	- Agrimony, Bilberry, Blackberry, Celery, Walnut, Yarrow
SWEATING, night sweats	- Sage
SWELLINGS SEE ALSO STINGS	- Agrimony, Carrot
TAPEWORM, intestinal	- Pomegranate, Wormwood
THROAT, inflammation of	- Sage
- sore	- Artichoke, Bilberry, Marshmallow
see also TRACHEITIS	
TONSILLITIS	- Artichoke
TOOTHACHE	- Elder
TRACHEITIS	- Mullein

ULCER
- duodenal — Comfrey
- mouth — Mulberry

URINARY
- system, complaints of — Stone fern
- tract, inflammation of — Couchgrass

URINE
- blood in — Agrimony
- sugar in — Lime
- retention of — Wormwood

VARICOSE
- ulcers — Purple loosestrife
- veins — Agrimony, Comfrey, Marigold

VOMITING — Agrimony, Spearmint

WARTS — Dandelion, Marigold, Walnut

WEAKNESS
see ATONY

WOUNDS — Ash, Cherry, Plantain, Purple loosestrife, Rosemary, Walnut, Yarrow
- septic — Agrimony, Garlic, Vervain, Yarrow
- slow-healing — Speedwell

WRINKLES — Lime

On the page opposite is Helleborus cyclophyllus, *known popularly in Greece as* Skarphi, *which is very similar to the* Ellevoros ton Antikiron *with which the shepherd-seer Melampus is said to have cured the daughters of King Protos of Argos, who had come to believe that they were cows.*

THE PLANTS
AND THEIR USES

1. Agrimony
Cocklebur, Stickwort

Greek names: Agrimoniá, asprozáki, phonóhorto
Latin name: *Agrimonia eupatoria*

Description: Erect perennial with stems 20-80 cm tall, tinged with red and hairy. Each leaf has many divisions of varying size on both sides of the central rib (pinnate). They are a brownish green above, and grey-green and very hairy on the underside. The yellow, five-petalled flowers are 1 cm in diameter.

Uses and preparations

— MIGRAINE, DYSPEPSIA, DIARRHOEA, COLIC, VOMITING, NEPHRITIS, CHRONIC PULMONARY CATARRH, CACHEXY

23

(general lassitude of organism), HAEMATURIA (blood in the urine), DERMATOLOGICAL COMPLAINTS, RHEUMATISM, JAUNDICE, DROPSY, LIVER and SPLEEN COMPLAINTS: Make an infusion, using a handful of fresh or dried agrimony to 1 litre of water, and drink the resulting tisane two or three times a day.

— PHARYNGITIS, BRONCHITIS, COUGH: Boil 100 gr of agrimony in 1 litre of water, until the liquid has been reduced to one-third of its original volume. After straining, add 50 g honey. Use as a gargle.

— SUGAR DIABETES: Make an infusion as above for migraine etc., and drink as a tea, at the same time observing the appropriate dietary regimen.

— SPRAINS, SWELLINGS, BRUISES and CONTUSIONS: Simmer equal volumes of agrimony leaves, bran (husks of ripe cereals), and vinegar. When the mixture becomes sticky, cool and spread on the affected area and leave as long as possible. Repeat frequently until relief has been obtained.

— SEPTIC WOUNDS: Take crushed leaves and mix them to a paste with pork fat. Put this paste on the wound, cover with gauze, and leave for several hours. Apply freshly made mixture daily until wound has stopped suppurating.

— DYSENTERY: This is relieved by drinking a little wine to which have been added crushed seeds of agrimony, or crushed parts of all the plant above ground, and left to steep.

— VARICOSE VEINS, PHLEBITIS: Crush fresh leaves in a mortar and put on affected area regularly every evening.

Habitat: In damp locations, in woodlands, highland villages, along forest roads. Widespread in all of mainland Greece.

Directions for gathering: The plant itself is best collected in summer when it flowers. Dry in the shade. The seeds are also used and must be collected later when ripe.

NOTES This is probably the *eupatorium* (hemp agrimony) mentioned by Dioscurides, and was believed to be an antidote for snake bite. Pliny says that Mithridates Eupator, King of Pontus, used the plant as an antidote to poisoning.

Agrimony contains tannin, a little volatile oil, and resin.

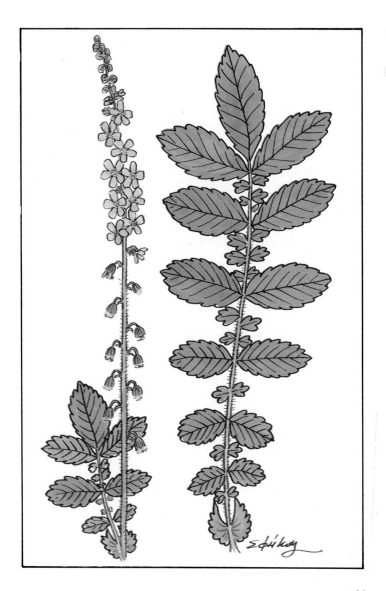

2. Artichoke
Cardoon

Greek name: Anginára
Latin name: *Cynara cardunculus*

Description: This is a familiar plant in its cultivated form, but in Greece it also exists growing wild. It is a very spiny perennial, the leathery leaves of which have a broad base and divide out into many sections (pinnately cut lobes), all of them with a spiny tip. The flower stalks are 50 cm to 1.50 m high, with smaller leaves growing up them. The flowers themselves are borne in globular heads, which in immaturity (the stage when they are eaten as a vegetable) are surrounded by oval bracts, again with spikes at the tips. It is the soft base of all but the extreme outer bracts, as well as the core, (the 'heart' of the plant), and the inner stem, which are edible.

Uses and preparations

— FEVER, STIFF JOINTS: Make a decoction from the green flower heads and the leaves by boiling for 20-30 minutes, and drink one or two glasses of the resulting liquid daily.
— SORE THROATS: The leaves are finely chopped and mixed with butter to make a stiff paste which is applied thickly externally to the throat. Tie with a cloth and leave as long as possible.
— TONSILLITIS: Boil leaves in a minimum of water until they are soft, and apply to the throat externally as a poultice.
— HAEMORRHOIDS: Make a poultice with crushed, raw leaves and apply externally.

Habitat: Wild on sandy sea-shores, cultivated in gardens or obtainable from greengrocers.

Directions for gathering: Collect green closed flower heads (buds) and leaves in spring.

NOTES Artichoke contains calcium, phosphorus and vitamins A, B, and C.
The plant is well known to have been cultivated in the time of Theophrastus.

3. Ash

Common ash, Weeping ash

Greek names: Melliós, Megálos phráxos
Latin name: *Fraxinus excelsior*

Description: Deciduous tree up to 40 m in full maturity. Easily identified by its black leaf buds. Leaves consist of 7-15 pointed elliptical leaflets right and left of a central rib (pinnate). The very small brownish-purple flowers grow in dense, rounded clusters and appear before the leaves; the hanging seeds are supplied with narrow, wing-shaped membranes. The smaller *F. ornus* (Manna, or Flowering ash) has more conspicuous white flowers borne in massed spikes and rather grey-green leaves, and is believed to share the pharmaceutical attributes of Common ash.

Uses and preparations

— WOUNDS and SORES: Cut a few twigs or small branches from the tree, peel them, and boil the fresh bark before applying as a poultice to the affected area.

— HYPERTENSION, FEVER: Make an infusion from not too dry ash bark, and drink at least once a day.

— DROPSY, KIDNEY and BLADDER DISORDERS: Make an infusion by bringing to the boil two to three tablespoons of dried chopped leaves in half a litre of cold water, and allow to stand. Drink as a diuretic.

Habitat: Grows in the mountain forests of northern Greece.

Directions for gathering: The bark may be collected any time of the year, the leaves from May to July. Remove the leaflets from the central rib and dry in the shade at less than 40° C.

NOTES Ash leaves contain flavonoids and derivatives of coumarin. The mannite ín the bark, used to make essence of manna, has a sweet taste, earning the tree is Greek name which is based on the word for honey.

4. Balm

Bawm, Lemon balm, Sweet balm

Greek names: Melissóhorto, mélissa, melissáki, melis-
sovótano
Latin name: *Melissa officinalis*

Description: Small, perennial shrubby herb, growing larger every year to become 30-80 cm in height. Stems are squarish, increasingly branching towards the top; leaves are oval to heart-shaped with toothed edges. The small, two-lipped white or pink flowers grow in clusters in the upper leaf axils. The entire plant, and the leaves especially, give off a strong, clear lemon aroma.

Uses and preparations

— HEART PAINS: Make an infusion with 50 g fresh or dried balm and 50 g wormwood *(Artemisia absinthium) (q.v.)* in 200 g water, and drink one glassful of the liquid every day for three days.

— NERVOUS IRRITABILITY, ANOREXIA (lack of appetite), INSOMNIA, HYSTERIA, FLATULENCE: Pour 1 litre boiling water on to 5-25 g of fresh or dried balm leaves, and drink a glassful of this infusion every morning.

Habitat: Grows all over Greece and is much cultivated in village gardens.

Directions for gathering: Should be collected in spring before it flowers, when the scent is most marked. Dry in the shade at less than 35° C, and as quickly as possible, since slow drying turns the leaves brown and affects the active constituents.

NOTES Balm contains linoleic and geranic acid, aldehyde, tannic and bitter essence, mucilage, as well as volatile oil. Pharmaceutically it goes under the name of *folia melissae.*

The *Aqua d'argento* of the Italians is a drink made by adding oils from balm and wormwood to a water base. Theophrastus and Dioscurides mention the plant as *melissóphyllon.* The current Greek name of *melissóhorto* (honey plant) also covers the plants

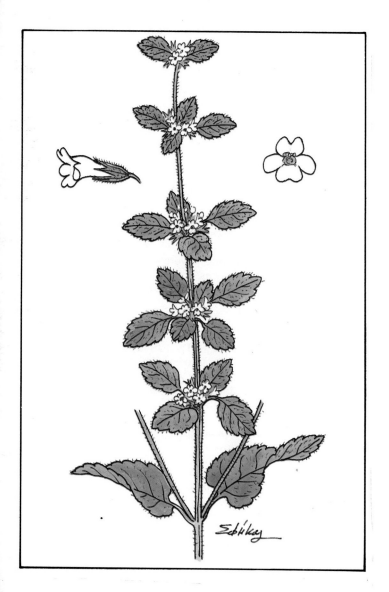

of the genus *heliotropium,* which have greyish-green leaves thickly felted with down, and small white flowers smelling of honey.

5. Basil

Greek name: *Vasilikós*
Latin name: *Ocymum basilicum*

Description: Basil is universally known and grown in Greece, mostly for culinary purposes. A pot of basil is also said to keep away the flies. The much-branched, low plant has little elliptical or oval leaves, and small white flowers which form tufts at the end of the stems. There are scores of varieties with small, medium, and relatively large leaves. The entire plant gives off a delicate aromatic smell.

Uses and preparations

— ABDOMINAL SPASMS, NERVOUS STOMACH, MIGRAINE, FAILING MEMORY: Make an infusion with fresh or dried leaves and stems, and drink the tisane while still lukewarm.

— CONSTIPATION: Make a salad with the tender shoots of fresh basil, and eat with oil added.

Habitat: Grows in all Greek gardens. Plants can be bought from nursery-men and from flower shops.

Directions for gathering: May be collected throughout the summer, but is most efficacious when it is about to flower.

NOTES This plant contains some well-known antiseptic properties.

Soaking a few leaves in water will prevent it from becoming brackish. In Greek country churches, balm is used in the preparation of Holy water.

6. Bearberry
Mountain-box

Greek names: Arkoudostáphilo, arkoudokoúmaro
Latin name: *Arctostaphylos uva-ursi*

Description: As its secondary English name implies, this is a small evergreen shrub, with low spreading branches and only up to 1 m high. (It is quite easily confused with Cowberry or Red whortleberry. *Vaccinium vitis idaea,* which has erect terminal shoots, however.)The leaves are small, lance-shaped or rounded, thick and leathery, the veins standing out strongly on the underside. The pink or white flowers are small and bell-shaped, with a rolled-back tooth-edged lip. The fruit is a round red berry the size of a pea, and has an acid taste.

Uses and preparations
— CYSTITIS, PYELITIS, GALL STONES, GALL SAND, GONORRHEA, KIDNEY and BLADDER INFECTIONS: Make a cold infusion with 10-30 g of finely chopped fresh leaves, or use coarse power from dried leaves, to 1 litre water. Just leave to stand, do not heat. Add a little bicarbonate of soda to one cupful taken morning and evening. Prolonged use may result in constipation because of the tannin content of the leaves, and misuse can cause temporary poisoning.

Habitat: Bearberry used to be quite common in highland locations in northern Greece. Unfortunately, intensive gathering of the plant has already made it disappear from many places where once it flourished.

Directions for gathering: This plant has its strongest therapeutic effect if collected in August. Cut branches (don't pull out the plant) with leaves and fruit, and dry them either in sun or shade. Store in a well-sealed glass jar.

NOTES Bearberry contains arbutin and methyl arbutine, which in certain physical conditions produce substances related to

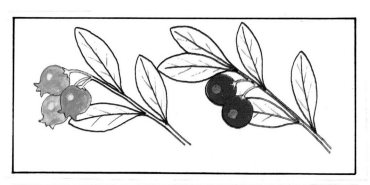

phenol, making the plant an antiseptic. The presence of flavonoids acts as a mild diuretic.

7. Bilberry
Blaeberry, Blueberry, Huckleberry, Wortleberry

Greek names: Vakkínio, Phínghi
Latin name: *Vaccinium myrtillus*

Description: Very low, partly woody, deciduous shrub with smooth, elliptical or oval leaves, the edges of which are finely toothed. Small, roundly bell-shaped, greenish-pink flowers. The pea-sized berries are purplish-black, fleshy and juicy, and contain many seeds each.

Uses and preparations
— THROAT AND MOUTH INFLAMMATION: Use a decoction, made from 1 tablespoonful of dried fruits boiled for five minutes in two tumblers of water, as a mouthwash and for gargling.
— DIARRHOEA, ENTERITIS: Let 50-100 g of dried leaves (some authorities say berries) swell in water, bring to the boil, cool, and drink. Berries may also be taken dried if chewed very well.
— SUGAR DIABETES: Soak the leaves (which contain a substance which very slightly lowers the level of blood sugar) in lukewarm water and leave for 24 hours. Strain the liquid and drink one small glassful a day.

Habitat: In mountainous locations in northern Greece, and in woodlands close to the alpine zone.

Direction for gathering: Collect in summer when the fruit is ripe. Cut small branches (don't pull out the plant) complete with leaves and berries, dry and store.

NOTE The chief active principle of the plant is tannin. It is therefore an antidiarrhoeal, especially when dried.

8. Blackberry
Bramble

Greek names: Vatomouriá, avatsiniá, vatsaniá
Latin name: *Rubus fruticosus*

Description: Very well-known rambling plant, with leaves divided into three separate segments (trifoliate), carried on long drooping branches well provided with large thorns. The pale pink five-petalled flowers develop into the purple-black composite berry, made up of many little juicy seed-sacks arranged densely round a pithy core.

Uses and preparations
— SUGAR DIABETES: In addition to adhering to a strict diet, a small glass of an infusion may be given each morning on an empty stomach, made from the tender ends, leaves and all, of the branches. Use two to three branch tips for each small glassful of water.
— DIARRHOEA, ANAEMIA: Make a decoction from two to three branch tips per small glassful of water, and drink as required.

Habitat: Anywhere at roadsides, on walls and fences, and in rocky scrubland.

Directions for gathering: Leaves may be collected at any time of the year before they are shed in late autumn.

NOTES This species is the *vátos* or *hamaívatos* of Theophrastus. The plant contains tannin, flavine, vitamin C, a bitter glycosin etc.; the fruit has organic acids, pectin, anthocyanin and sugar.

9. Burdock

Lesser burdock, Thorny burr, Beggar's button

Greek name: Láppa
Latin name: *Arctium lappa*

Description: Large biennial forming a basal rosette of leaves in the first year, and branched and flowering stalks in the second. Roots are up to 5 cm thick, and grow vertically down. Leaves are large, ovate, and pointed. The small elongated red flowers emerge from a thistly ball of bracts, each of which has a stiff, hooked tip. These make up the ball-like structure which clings to rough surfaces such as cloth.

Uses and preparations

— SPOTS and PIMPLES: Make a decoction of two to three tablespoonsful of chopped dried root in 1 litre of water, and drink the liquid. Alternatively, powder the dried root and take 1 tablespoonful in water three times daily.
— LOSS OF HAIR, BALDING: See Rosemary.

Habitat: Roadsides and uncultivated places all over Greece.

Directions for gathering: Collect the root from first-year plants in autumn, from second-year plants in spring. Split lengthways and dry at less than 70° C.

NOTES Burdock contains a small amount of volatile oil, resin, and several antibiotic substances. It is diuretic and increases resistance to infections.

10. Camomile
Chamomile, Wild chamomile, Matricaria

Greek names: Hamomíli, hamómilo, panairítsa (in Polygyros), louloúdi t'Ai 'Yorgioú
Latin name: *Matricaria chamomilla*

Description: An erect, branched small annual with extremely finely feathered leaves (two to three times pinnate) and flowers borne at the tips of the stems. Newly opened they look very much like daisies, later on the petals droop towards the back as the yellow centres expand and become more conically domed.

Uses and preparations

— CONSTIPATION, STOMACH CRAMP, COLDS, OBESITY, NEURALGIA: Make a cold infusion by soaking one tablespoonful of the flowers in a litre of cold water. Do not heat. For obesity, do not neglect the dietary regimen.

— FLACCID SKIN (facial), SKIN IMPURITIES: Steam the face with a hot infusion of dried camomile flowers as described for Sage (q.v.)

— INFLAMED SKIN, INFLAMED EYES: Make compresses with an infusion of dried camomile flowers while it is still warm, and leave on the affected area as long as possible.

Habitat: Very common throughout Greece on cultivated and fallow land, waste places, etc., preferring warm sunny locations.

Directions for gathering: Collect flowers in spring when petals are fully expanded, and dry in the shade at less than 35° C.

NOTES Camomile flowers, pharmaceutically *flores chamomilae*, contain volatile oils including the relatively rare dark-blue hamazulenium, mucilage etc. Many of the active constituents are widely used in the manufacture of cosmetics.

11. Carrot

Greek names: Karótto, réfki, défki (Corfu), pastináka,
kavoútsi, havoútsi, voútsi (Cyprus)
Latin name: *Daucus carota*

Description: As well as the cultivated form, Greece also has the
wild carrot, a hairy, erect biennial. Its feathery leaves (three times
pinnate) resemble those of the edible variety. The small flowers
are borne in a cluster structured rather like an open umbrella.
This 'umbel' is white or pink, often purplish at the centre. The
plant is very well known in its cultivated form for its fleshy, red,
edible tap root.

Uses and prepations

— BURNS, SWELLINGS: Finely grate fresh carrot and put the
paste on the affected area.

— ARTHRITIS, RHEUMATISM, WEAK EYE SIGHT, GALL
COMPLAINTS: Boil chopped carrots and drink of the juice at
least once a day.

Habitat: Available from shops almost all the year round.

Directions for use: Use the fresh tap root, i.e. the carrot.

NOTES Carrot contains calcium, iron, magnesium, phosphorus,
iodine, chlorine, cobalt, vitamin C and pro-vitamin A, sulphur,
potassium, sodium, and bromine.

12. Celery

Greek name: Sélino
Latin name: *Apium graveolens*

Descriptions: The plant with this Latin name is the wild-growing variety of the celery generally known as a kitchen vegetable. It is a much-branched biennial up to 80 cm tall, with shiny leaves like those of the cultivated form, and especially the lower leaves divided into three tooth-edged sections each (trifoliate). The stems are grooved, and the very small greenish-white flowers are borne in loose, domed compound heads (umbels). The fruits are very small ribbed ovoids.

Uses and preparations

— FEVER: Crush raw leaves and drink the resulting juice.
— DYSPEPSIA, ARTHRITIS, AEROPHAGIA: Boil a teaspoonful of seeds in one teacupful of water for a few minutes, let stand, and drink some of the liquid two to three times a day. Make freshly each day.
— RHEUMATISM, SUGAR DIABETES, STIFF JOINTS: Make a decoction from a piece of chopped fresh or dried root, and drink the liquid daily.

Habitat: Celery grows wild in Greece only on the seashore, in salt-rich, sandy soils. It is much cultivated in kitchen gardens and fields, and in season can be bought from greengrocers (except for the root and seeds).

Directions for gathering: Leaves and roots may be collected any time except in winter; the seeds ripen in summer.

NOTES For the ancient Greeks, celery was associated with funeral rites, the mourners accompanying the dead to their final resting place carrying wreaths of celery which were then put on the grave. Celery was also used to crown athletes in the Neméan Games, held in memory of Archémonas, son of the King of Neméa, who died of the bite of a snake which had been concealed in some celery.

13. Cherry

Wild cherry, Gean

Greek names: Kerasiá, agriokerasiá
Latin name: *Prunus avium*

Description: This is the ancestor of the cultivated cherry. The medium-sized deciduous tree has a glistening, reddish, horizontally fissured bark, and bunches of long-stalked white flowers in spring with bright orange-tipped stamens. The leaves are elliptical, pointed, and have toothed edges. The cultivated tree has very similar characteristics.

Uses and preparations

— ADENOPATHY (disease of the glandular system): Take 50 g of cherry gum (the resin from the trunk of the tree), 50 g mastic, 50 g cinnamon, 10 g quinine, 100 g sugar and 1 cypress cone, and boil in 1 kg brusque red wine until only 600-700 g remain. Of this liquid drink 1 wineglassful morning, noon and night before meals.

— BURNS, WOUNDS: Boil half a kilo fresh or dried cherry leaves in half a litre of wine. When cool, place the boiled leaves on the affected area for 10 minutes, then remove and anoint with resin oil.

— WEAKNESS, GENERAL DEBILITY: Put some pieces of cherry gum into a bottle of water and shake for a while. Drink this water whenever you are thirsty.

Habitat: Common in all Greek mountain woodlands at medium altitudes.

Directions for gathering: Leaves and gum can be collected at any time during the growing-season, and may also be taken from cultivated trees. Their potency is highest, however, in late spring to early summer. The gum is obtained by making incisions in the bark, from which it will ooze out slowly and coagulate into beads for collection later.

14. Coltsfoot
Coughwort, Horse hoof, Foal's foot, Ass' foot, Bull's foot

Greek names: Hamólefka, víhio
Latin name: *Tussilago farfara*

Description: A low perennial with subterranean shoots spreading rapidly. Flowering stems of up to 20 cm appear in spring before the main leaves, and are covered with small, narrow and purple scaly leaves. The yellow flowers resemble those of the dandelion structurally, but are smaller and stiffer and, as it were, more neatly trimmed. The leaves form a basal rosette and are heart-shaped, with irregular edges, dark green above, gray-green on the underside with a dense felty covering of hairs.

Uses and preparations

— ASTHMA: Burn dried flowers and leaves and inhale the smoke. This will relieve asthmatic attacks.

— CARBUNCLES, SPOTS, BOILS: Boil some dried flowers and apply as a mildly effective poultice.

— COUGH, BRONCHITIS: Make an infusion with one or two tablespoonsful of dried flowers to 1 litre of water and drink regularly.

Habitat: Sandy as well as clay soils in almost all elevated regions of Greece, in damp but sunny locations.

Directions for gathering: Collect flower heads in very early spring, the leaves later. Flowers must be dried in the shade, the leaves may also be dried in sunlight.

NOTES The medicinal properties of coltsfoot have been known since antiquity. The ancient Greeks called the plant *vihion* or *hamailéfki.*

15. Comfrey
Boneset, Knitbone, Bruisewort

Greek names: Stekoúli, hondroútsiko, afti tou gáidarou
Latin name: *Symphytum officinale*

Descriptions: A perennial plant up to 60 cm in height. The leaves are up to 20 cm long, lance-shaped ovals, and very hairy on the underside (earning it the Greek name of Donkey's ear). Leaves lower down have short leafstalks. Erect hollow stems branch in the upper part only. The white, pink, or purple flowers are tubular, 1.5 cm long, with short, turned-back lips. They grow in close succession towards the ends of the stems which at first terminate in a tight curl, but later lengthen and straighten out. The roots are up to 2 cm thick, brownish-black outside, white inside.

Uses and preparations

— LIGHT BURNS, CRACKED NIPPLES: Squeeze the glutinous juice from the fresh root and stems of the plant, and apply to the affected area.

— PHLEBITIS, GOUT, BRUISES, VARICOSE VEINS: Apply compresses of fresh grated root, or of dried powdered root made into a paste with the addition of water.

— DIAORRHEA, DYSENTERY, DUODENAL ULCER: Make a tisane of 15-60 g of dried or fresh grated root to 1 litre of water — or alternatively mix one to three teaspoons of powdered root with water — and drink two to three times a day until symptoms have passed.

Habitat: Common in northern Greece in damp locations, in ditches, on river banks etc.

Directions for gathering: Collect stems and leaves in spring and summer. Roots are taken in autumn when the top of the plant has died down and before new growth starts. Slice lengthwise and dry in the sun, or artificially at 40-50° C.

NOTES This plant, and especially the root which was known as *radex symphyti,* was once used to set broken bones. Comfrey

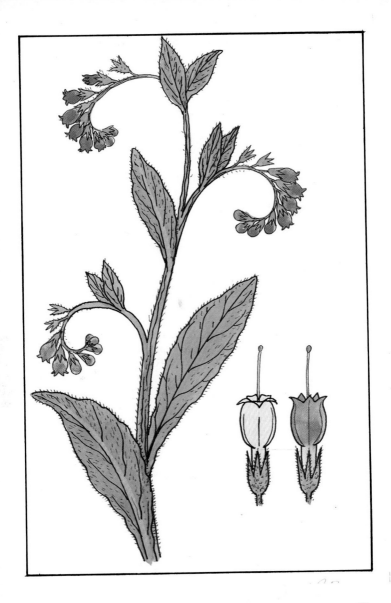

contains tannin, resin, gallic acid, volatile oil, allantoin and traces of alkaloids.

16. Couchgrass
Quick-grass, Twitch-grass

Greek names: Agriáda, aíra
Latin name: *Agropyrum repens*

Description: Perennial weed with thin roots which send out subterranean runners (rhizomes) in all directions and continually throw up new shoots. When in flower, these resemble small flat ears of wheat. Flowers and seeds grow right and left of a zig-zag axis, but without the beard-like awns of wheat, and much more loosely. The long leaves are very narrow, smooth and pointed.

Uses and preparations
— RHEUMATISM; INFLAMMATION OF THE BLADDER, KIDNEY and URINARY TRACT; GALL and LIVER COMPLAINTS: Make a decoction from the fresh or dried rhizomes, using 1 litre of cold water to one or to tablespoonful of chopped root, boil for 10 minutes, let stand for half an hour, and drink the liquid.
— See also Globe thistle for NEURASTHENIA.

Habitat: In fields and at road sides all over Greece.

Directions for gathering: Collect in summer. All of the plant may be used, but especially the rhizome roots.

NOTES Couchgrass roots contain glucose, tricitin (carbohydrate related to starch), and salts of potassium.

In times of wheat shortage, the ancient Egyptians used the flour obtained from grinding up couchgrass roots to mix with their ordinary flour to stretch it.

17. Dandelion

Greek names: Pikralída, agriomároulo, radíki tou vounoú,
pikrorádiko

Latin name: *Taraxacum officinale*

Description: A low variable plant with relatively long pointed leaves more or less heavily indented on each side of the central rib, the edges usually resembling a row of irregular sharp teeth. All the leaves grow from the top of a long, blackish-brown tap root and form a basal rosette which may lie flat on the ground or be semi-erect. The yellow flowers grow singly on often pinkish, long, very smooth hollow stalks, and structurally resemble small, flat double chrysanthemums. They form the characteristic round seed heads known as dandelion lanterns — each seed, attached at the centre of the globe to a softly leathery stud, being provided with a stalk and topped with a tuft of spreading hairs which act like parachutes during wind dispersal. The milky white sap of the plant is rather bitter and stains the skin brown. The many different varieties with diverse forms have not, so far, been examined for possibly different medicinal properties.

Uses and preparations

SPOTS and PIMPLES, SWELLINGS FROM BEE STINGS, MOLES, WARTS: Express the milky sap from the fresh root, and apply to the skin once a day.

KIDNEY STONES, CHRONIC DERMATITIS, ARTHRITIS, SWOLLEN LIVER, SWOLLEN SPLEEN due to malaria, SCURVY, GLANDULAR MISFUNCTIONING, MENTAL FATIGUE, HEPATITIC DROPSY, CHRONIC EXCEMA: Make an infusion from finely chopped fresh or dried plants (one or two tablespoonsful to half a litre of water) after first having let them soak for two hours. Drink the juice in place of plain water three times a day.

GENERAL FATIGUE of the ORGANISM after illness or overwork: Boil one whole plant each of fresh or dried dandelion, nettle *(q.v.)*, and yarrow *(q.v.)* in a small saucepan of water, and drink the decoction, after having let it stand, at least once a day in place of plain water.

RHEUMATISM: Boil 10 g dried root in 200 g water for 15 minutes, and drink a wineglassful of the liquid twice a day.

Habitat: Widespread especially in northern Greece in uncultivated soils or in fields. In southern Greece, dandelion is mostly
found in mountain grassland.

Directions for gathering: Should not be collected during the hot
part of the year (July to September) when the roots are very bitter
(though certain herbals specify that this is exactly the time when
they should be gathered). The best time is in spring, a little before
the flowers emerge. Parts used are the dried root (large roots may
need splitting lengthwise before drying in either shade or

sunlight); also the entire plant including the root, if gathered in spring.

NOTES The roots of dandelion contain latex and inulin in large amounts, and the active principles of the plant need further study. Dandelion stimulates the digestive glands, and especially the pancreas and bile ducts.

18. Elder
Black elder

Greek names: Samboúkos, koufoxyliá, phroxylánthi, aphroxyliá
Latin name: *Sambucus nigra*

Description: Large deciduous shrub with five leaflets on every main leaf-rib (pinnate). The branches have soft bark around abundant soft white pith. The tiny white flowers are borne in large, flat compound discs (false umbels) and are very sweet-smelling. The fruits are very small purplish-black berries with red juice.

Uses and preparations
— PULMONARY CATARRH, ANGINA, PECTORIS: Drink an infusion (one litre of boiling water poured on to one to two tablespoonsfuls of dried flowers) which has been allowed to stand.
— INFLAMMATION OF THE SKIN, CARBUNCLES, ERYSIPELAS (St Anthony's fire, the rose): Use the above infusion and gently massage the affected area with it as a liniment.
— EXCEMA: Make an infusion of two tablespoonsful of dried alder leaves to one litre of water, soak some lint in this liquid, and apply as a compress. The tisane may also be drunk.
— TOOTHACHE: Use the infusion given for Catarrh above as a mouthwash, retaining the liquid in the mouth for as long as possible.
— INFLUENZA: Pour boiling water on to half a handful of dried elder flowers and a sprig of dried mint *(q.v.)*, allow to stand,

and drink the still warm tisane before retiring at night.

— CONSTIPATION: Take the fruits by the tablespoonful, either fresh or as a jam; they will act as a natural laxative.

Habitat: Elder grows almost anywhere, cultivated as well as wild. Plants from elevated locations are particularly effective.

Directions for gathering: The leaves may be collected all through the summer; the flowers are taken when fully open and dried as quickly as possible in the shade at less than 40° C; the berries are gathered when fully ripe.

NOTES The flowers of this plant (pharmaceutically known as *flores sambuci)* as well as the leaves contain volatile oil, mucilage, and flavonoid glycosides. An additional constituent of the ripe berries is the anti-pneumonic vitamin C2-Euler, while bark and green berries contain prussic acid in glucoside form and are toxic.

19. Elm

Field elm

Greek names: Karagátsi, phteliá, phteliós, vrissós, vrissiá, kambophteliá
Latin name: *Ulmus campestris*

Description: A large straight tree, often with many suckers, and with dark-grey bark which in mature specimens has longitudinal fissures and striations. The base of the leaves is asymmetrical, as it they had been carelessly made. They are oval in shape with a pointed tip and saw-edged, smooth above but slightly hairy on the underside. The bunched seeds are each centred in a flat papery membrane (see illustration).

Uses and preparations
— ANAEMIA: Take 500 g dried young bark, 100 g quinine, 100 g sugar, 100 g whole fresh or dried celery *(q.v.)*, 50 g cinnamon, and two cypress cones. Boil all together and strain well. Drink three glasses of this liquid per day.
— ASTHMA: Make a decoction of young, dried or fresh elm bark, together with figwort *(Scrophularia canina)* and sugar. Strain through a cloth, not a metal strainer, and drink one wineglassful every morning, mixed well with a beaten egg.
— FAST HEARTBEAT: Boil up one kilo of young bark of elm, one kilo dandelion *(q.v.)*, and half a kilo sow thistle *(Sonchus oleraceus)* in water, and eat without adding salt. Keep the juice, and drink at the rate of two wineglassesful a day.
See also Globe thistle and Horsemint for NEURASTHENIA.

Habitat: Elm trees grow anywhere in the Greek forests, in the mountains and on the plains, though more frequently in the north than in the south. They are also often to be found in city parks.

Directions for gathering: The elm bark can be collected at any time of the year, but best in spring before the leaves emerge. Take only young bark, as the old, fissured bark contains almost no active constituents.

NOTES In Homer's time, elm was known as *pteléï*. Theophratus and Dioscurides later called it *pteléa*.

The bark contains abundant mucilage and tannin, and is astringent and anti-inflammatory.

61

20. Garlic

Greek name: Skórdo
Latin name: *Allium sativum*

Description: A perennial plant with a compound bulb made up of several partial bulbs (cloves) enclosed in a common white, papery membrane. The erect, single stem has long narrow leaves with rough edges. At its top it forms an onion-shaped globe in a papery membrane with a long terminal spike, which eventually bursts lengthways to release a round bouquet of small white or pinkish flowers. The bulb is well known as a flavouring, especially in mediterranean cuisine.

Uses and preparations

— ARTHRITIS: Take four whole bulbs of garlic, peel, and crush in a mortar. Put the resulting paste on the affected area, bandage, and leave for 12 hours. Alternatively, boil well one kilo of garlic bulbs in one kilo oil, strain the oil and add 50 g of turpentine and four broken egg yolks. Mix well and use frequently as a liniment.

— SEPTIC WOUNDS: Make a poultice of crushed garlic bulbs and tie to the wound.

— HYPERTENSION: One clove of raw garlic a day will help to lower the blood pressure. If taken whole like a pill, there will be none of the objectionable odour on the breath.

— OBESITY: Eat one clove of raw garlic every morning. Swallow whole (see above).

Habitat: In fields and kitchen gardens, and available from any greengrocer.

Directions for gathering: Uproot when the leaves have withered, and store the bulb in a dry place.

NOTES Garlic has been universally acknowledged since very ancient times for its medicinal properties. Pliny and Dioscurides list it as effective against a great variety of ailments, and even thought it would cure snake bite. (Folk superstition has

considered it a valuable preventive against vampires.) Today it is used pharmaceutically in various preparations against malaria.

21. Germander

Greek names: Stomahovótano, panayióhorto, amárandos, votáni tis agápis, tis kirás to hortári, tis panayiás to hortári, mytéra, livanóhorto
Latin name: *Teucrium polium*

Description: A very variable species of perennial shrubby plant, 10-30 cm high and closely branched. The stems and leaves are densely covered with hairs, giving the plant a grey, felt-covered appearance. The leaves are rather narrow and often have inrolled edges. The tiny flowers form either globular heads or spikes at the ends of the stems. They are pink or white, or occasionaly yellowish; the petals rise from a tubular throat and split into two at the lip (see sketch).

Uses and preparations

— ATONY (lassitude), INFLAMMATION OF STOMACH LINING and INTESTINES: Make a tisane by pouring half a litre of boiling water on two tablespoonsful of chopped dried flowering stems and leaves, allow to stand, and drink the liquid at least twice a day. Honey may be added to improve the otherwise rather bitter taste.

Habitat: Almost anywhere in Greece in stony locations or open sunny grassland at medium altitude.

Directions for gathering: Collect in July when in flower, and dry in the shade at less than 35° C.

NOTES Hippocrates and Dioscurides both praised germander for its medicinal properties. Theophrastus called it *pólion* and said it protects clothes against moths.

Germander contains volatile oil, saponin, a tannic substance, resin, chromic matter, flavonoids and bitter substances.

22. Globe thistle

Greek names: Stavrángatho, skoliámbri, ahinángatho,
ahinóhorto, moshokoúli, kamilángatho
(Cyprus)
Latin name: *Echinops viscosus*

Description: This erect, stiff, thistly perennial plant retains a
basal rosette of deeply tooth-edged leaves through the winter
months. Each of the leaf projections ends in a spine. The new,
tender leaves are green with white splotches. In the spring,
branched flower stems shoot up from the basal rosette, ending in
round, prickly green heads.

Uses and preparations
— NEURASTHENIA (nervous debility): Make a decoction of
200 g dried globe-thistle leaves, 500 g coarsely powdered or
finely chopped dried bark of elm *(q.v.)*, and 200 g dried root of
couchgrass *(q.v.)*, in two litres of water. Strain, and drink one
waterglassful morning and evening.

Habitat: On uncultivated land, waste grounds and rocky places in
the hills of southern Greece.

Directions for gathering: Collect leaves in spring when the new
growth appears. Dry quickly.

23. Hawthorn, Common hawthorn, May, Whitethorn

Greek   names: Mourtsiá, boubouliá, trikoukiá, mou-
moun̄zeliá, glógos

Latin name: *Crataegus oxycantha* or *C. laevigata*

Description: Thorny shrub or small tree growing up to 5 m in height, with leaves more or less deeply divided into three-toothed lobes. The small, white, five-petalled flowers appear in pretty bouquet-like clusters in spring. The mealy fruits are 8-15 mm in diameter and a striking deep red when ripe.

Uses and preparations

— DIARRHOEA: Bring to the boil 10-15 fresh or dried berries per glassful of water, let stand, drain and drink the liquid as a tea.

— HEART IRREGULARITY, ARTERIOSCLEROSIS: Make an infusion with 10 g of the fresh or dried flowers to 1 litre of water, and drink some of this liquid once a day.

Habitat: On hillsides, in ravines and hedges in northern Greece. Hawthorn was thought to grow in the south also, but it was recently established that this is not Common hawthorn but *C. monogyna* which, however, may well have the same properties. It is very similar in appearance to the species above, but the leaves are more deeply divided into three to five lobes.

Directions for gathering: The flowers are collected in spring, the fruits from September to November. Both are used either fresh or dried.

NOTES The leaves, flowers and fruits of the plant contain flavone glycosides and catechins. The flowers additionally have volatile oil, tannin and triethyl.

Common hawthorn is probably the flowering mespilus, *mespíli,* mentioned by Theophrastus.

24. Hemlock

Greek names: Mangoúta, amárangos (Mani), askotsitsára
(Crete), kampoudiá (Cyprus), vromóhorto,
karpoúsa
Latin name: *Conium maculatum*

Description: An erect, much-branched biennial up to 1 m high,
smelling strongly of mice. The hollow stems are deeply furrowed,
and spotted characteristically with purple along their lower
parts. The leaves are very feathery (two to three times pinnate);
the small white flowers are borne in umbrella-like heads (umbels)
at the top of the stems.

Uses and preparation

— SHINGLES, ERYSIPELAS (St Anthony's fire or the rose),
PSORIASIS, CANCER of the SKIN: Make a poultice from the
crushed fresh leaves and apply to the affected area.

Warning: Although hemlock indisputably has therapeutic
properties for the treatment of lymphatic and glandular
swellings, it should not be taken internally because it is
poisonous and may prove fatal if used by laymen.

Habitat: At road sides, in waste grounds and fieds, and among
ruins in southern Greece and on the islands.

Directions for gathering: Collect in summer when fully
developed.

NOTES This is the plant called *kónio* in ancient times. Its juice is
poisonous in large quantities, but brings a painless death. The
philosopher Socrates, after he had been publicly condemned to
death for his teachings, drank hemock and died by his own hand.
The first to discover that this plant is a painless killer seems to
have been Thrasias from Mantinia.

Hemlock is known pharmaceutically as *herba conii maculati*.

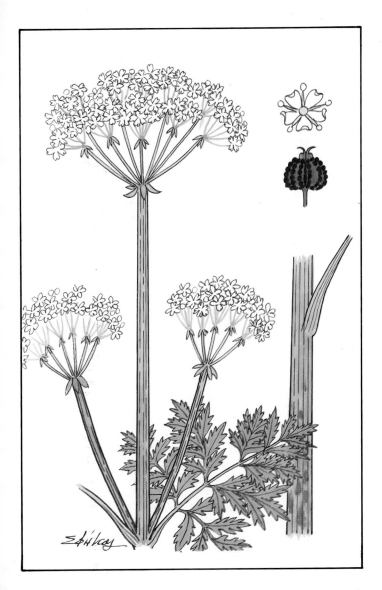

25. Horsemint

Greek names: Agriodiósmos, kalamíthra, kalamídi, potamogítanos (Cyprus), ménda.
Latin name: *Mentha longifolia*

Description: A species of mint easily recognised by its dense covering of silky green-white down. The leaves are oval and stalkless, and have finely saw-toothed edges. The root system spreads in all directions underground and continually sends up new shoots above ground. These grow up to 30 cm tall, ending in cylindrical flower spikes consisting of many small white, pinkish or purplish flowers. The whole plant gives off a strong aromatic odour of mint.

Uses and preparations

— RHEUMATISM: Take half a kilo of dried horsemint, a kilo dried whole celery plant *(q.v.)*, one handful seeds of common juniper *(q.v.)*, and make a decoction in same volume of water. Drink three glasses of the resulting tisane daily for two months.

— NEURASTHENIA (nervous debility): Make an infusion with 100 g dried or fresh horsemint, 100 g dried bark of elm *(q.v.)*, 100 g quinine, and 100 g sugar to one liter water. Drink three wineglassesful per day.

Habitat: In damp highland locations in southern Greece. In the north of the country, horsemint prefers moderate elevations and flat, damp places.

Directions for gathering: Collect flowering stems and root in spring, or at the beginning of summer when the plant is in flower.

NOTES This species may be the third of the *kalaminths* mentioned by Dioscurides. A similar species is *mentha rotundifolia* (apple-scented mint), which has more rounded leaves, white or pink flowers, and grows in southern Greece as far down as Crete. Both species are also used in perfumery.

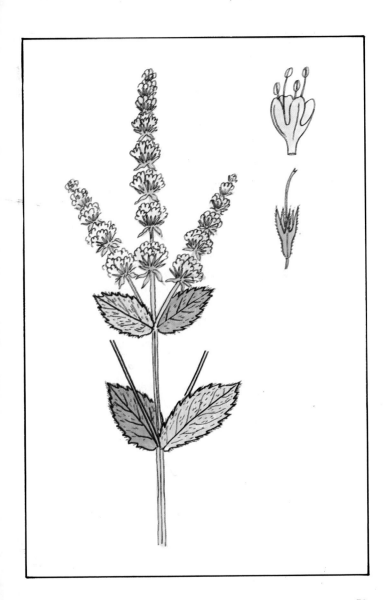

26. Juniper

Greek names: Vounókentro, kédro, árkefthos, agriokiparíssi, véni, agriókedro, kéntro
Latin name: *Juniperus communis*

Description: Small tree or shrub, rarely growing more than 5 m tall, and often found in Greece as a dwarf shrub, spreading along the ground. The needle-shaped leaves are hard and pointed. The round fruits mature only the third year after flowering. They start out resembling very small, black cypress cones, about 1 cm in diameter. When ripe, they look like a blue-black berry with a star-shaped fissure at the apex, and have a sweetish, resinous taste.

Uses and preparations

— STOMACH UPSETS, ANOREXY (loss of appetite), GENERAL FATIGUE OF THE ORGANISM: Drink a waterglassful a day of a tisane made from 5-10 bruised dried or fresh berries, or freshly cut wood (do not boil). This has a depurative effect and improves the appetite. Chewing 3-6 dried berries a day has a similar effect.

— SCIATICA, RHEUMATISM: Squeeze the fruits in a juicer and use the liquid as a liniment to gently massage the affected area.

Habitat: In mountainous locations above 1,500 m elevation.

Directions for gathering: Collect the mature berries in summer by beating the branches over a cloth. Dry them in a well-ventilated place.

NOTES This species is mentioned by Theophrastus under the name of *árkefthos*. The berries are pharmaceutically known as *baccae juniperi*.

The volatile oil contained in juniper acts as a diuretic and as a stimulant for the secretion of gastric juices.

27. Laurel

Sweet bay, Spurge laurel, Daphne

Greek names: Dáphny, váya, phylláda
Latin name: *Laurus nobilis*

Description: A large, evergreen shrub or small tree with gray bark and dark-green, lance-shaped, elliptical leaves, leathery, and highly aromatic when crushed. Small, four-petalled creamy flowers grow in clusters in the leaf axils. The fruits are black berries the size of small olives.

Uses and preparations

— ATONIC (depressive) DYSPEPSIA: Drink a decoction made from two or three fresh leaves per glassful of water.

— STOMACH SPASMS: Soak 4 g fresh laurel leaves to 8 g peel of bitter orange in 200 g of water for 15 minutes. Strain and sugar to taste. Use as a tisane.

Habitat: Common in the wild form, and also often found cultivated in parks and gardens.

Directions for gathering: The leaves may be collected any time of the year, but young leaves are most potent.

NOTES The active constituents of laurel are volatile oil, quinol, terpenes, methyeugenol, eugenol etc. The fruit contains volatile and fatty oil and is considered a tonic and styptic for the stomach; it goes under the pharmaceutical name of *fructus lauri siccati*.

28. Lemon

Greek name: Lemoniá
Latin name: *Citrus limonium*

Description: A small evergreen tree with glossy, pointed, elliptical leaves. Very well known for its fruit, and cultivated throughout Greece except in the highland regions. The flowers, which are strongly scented, have five fleshy, strap-shaped petals, white on the inside and tinged pink on the outside. The pharmaceutical properties of the tree are concentrated in the fruit, a yellow oval with a more or less thick rind over sour flesh enclosing the seeds.

Uses and preparations

— SEASICKNESS: Mix the juice from two lemons with a glass of seawater and drink.

— LOSS OF HAIR, BALDING: Rub affected area with lemon juice.

— INSOMNIA: Squeeze the juice from a lemon and an orange, add two spoonsful of honey, dissolve in a glass of cold water, and drink before retiring at night.

— CHOLESTEROL; Take lemon juice daily in quantities of one part lemon juice, three parts cold (never hot) water. Honey, but not sugar, may be added for sweetening.

Habitat: Everywhere in Greece in gardens and yards, and available from greengrocers.

Directions for acquiring: Lemons are obtainable all the year round, though they may be somewhat scarce at certain seasons. Several varieties fruit twice a year.

NOTES Lemon contains hesperics, aurantium, gallic acid, volatile oil, and many vitamins with a strong predominance of vitamin C.

29. Lime

Linden, Silver lime, Broad-leaved lime

Greek names: Tílio, phlamouriá, phlamoúri, lípa, philouriá
Latin name: *Tilia platyphyllos* and *T. tomentosa*

Description: These are two similar species of a large deciduous tree with heart-shaped, somewhat asymmetrical leaves. In both species, the underside of the leaves is hairy. *T. tomentosa* has the hairs growing in star formations, and its name of Silver lime is due to the contrast of the dark-green upper side of the leaf against the whitish-grey back. The strongly scented flowers appear in clusters from the top of a common, hanging stalk which for half its length is joined to a propeller-like bract. The seeds are small, round, dark brown capsules. The various cultivated limes have similar therapeutic qualities to the species listed here, but the flowers of Europe's *T. argentea* and of American lime cause vomiting and diarrhoea in some people.

Uses and preparations

— FRECKLES, WRINKLES: Pour a glassful of boiling water on 10-15 dried lime flowers, and allow to stand before applying the liquid in poultice form. (Do not boil, which will destroy the active principles of the flowers.)

— INSOMNIA, COLDS: Drink some of the infusion made as above.

— SCIATICA, LUMBAGO, GOUT, GLYCOSURIA (sugar in the urine), RHEUMATISM, ARTHRITIS: Boil 40 g of small pieces of chopped, dried young lime wood (not the bark only) in 1 litre of water until the volume is reduced to three-quarters of the original measure. Strain, and drink one or two glasses of the liquor early in the day.

Habitat: In Greece, lime trees grow wild only in the mountain forests, especially in the north. It is easier to find cultivated trees in city parks or squares.

Directions for gathering: The wood may be collected at any time, but best in spring. The flowers should be taken when they have

just opened; they must be dried in the shade and stored for no more than twelve months because they lose their potency.

NOTES Theophrastus mentions lime under the name of *philira.*
   The flowers contain the aromatic substance pharnesol, as well as tannin, mucilage, hesperic, wax, sugar etc.

30. Marigold
Calendula , Wild marigold

Greek names: Kaléndoula, nekroloúloudo
Latin name: *Calendula arvensis*

Description: This is an annual specie, very similar to the garden marigold *(C.officinalis* which may be used in the same way), though the flowers are much smaller, resembling yellow or orange daisies in shape and size. The leaves are lance-shaped to oblong, soft and hairy. *C. officinalis* has the same physical characteristics on a larger scale.

Uses and preparations
— ACNE: Blanch fresh leaves briefly in boiling water, and when cool apply as a poultice to the affected area.
— ECZEMA, ERYSIPELAS (St Anthony's fire, or the rose), WARTS: Make a decoction with 5-10 dried or fresh flower heads per glassful of water, and use the resulting liquid for compresses.
— DELAYED MENSTRUATION: Try an infusion with two teaspoonsful of flower petals or flowers to half a litre of water. Drink as tea.
— VARICOSE VEINS: Make a decoction from one or two springs with leaves and flower heads per glassful of water, and use for compresses.

Habitat: Very common in lowland areas, especially in hot regions.

Directions for gathering: Collect leaves and fully opened flower heads from February to April, and dry in the shade.

NOTES Active constituents of marigold are resin, a bitter principle, saponin, and traces of volatile oil.

31. Marshmallow
Althaea, Mallards

Greek names: Neromolóha, dendromolóha
Latin name: *Althaea officinalis*

Description: A perennial plant with one or more stems up to 2 m high, and densely covered all over with velvety hairs, giving it a silvery look. The stalked leaves are pointed ovals, slightly lobed into three sections. The five-petalled flowers resemble those of the single hollyhock and hibiscus; they are white or pinkish white, with numerous stamens tipped reddish-purple to dark violet, and grow from the leaf axils in the upper part of the tall stem.

Uses and preparations
— BRONCHITIS, PHARYNGITIS, COLDS: Make an infusion of two teaspoonsful of coarsely ground, peeled, dried root in half a litre of cold water, let stand 3-10 hours, sweeten with honey, and give to children or old people to drink. Alternatively, make a hot infusion of four spoonsful of either all dried flowers or half flowers half leaves per a glassful of water for general use, and drink while still hot.

— SORE THROAT: Take 10 g marshmallow leaves and one seedhead of field poppy, and make a decoction to which a little honey may be added. Gargle with the liquid while it is still warm.

— ENTERITIS, DYSENTERY: Decoct two teaspoonsful of peeled, coarsely ground dried root per half litre of water, and boil until the liquid is reduced to two-thirds of its original volume. Strain and drink while still lukewarm.

— BRUISES, CONTUSIONS, SKIN INFLAMMATIONS: Briefly boil dried flowers or leaves in a minimum of water, and when no longer scalding, apply as poultice to the affected area.

Habitat: Can be found in all parts of Greece, but prefers damp coastal locations, marshes, and moist ravines.

Directions for gathering: The best season for collecting leaves and flowers is in early summer when flowers are fully open. If it is

specifically the root which is required, this should be collected in late autumn, stored in a cool place, and subsequently peeled and dried at 50-60° C.

NOTES A common plant in ancient Greece when it was known under the names of *althéa* or *evískos*.

Marshmallow contains several active substances, especially so the root which has starch, gum, leucona, asparagine, sacharose and oil.

A species very similar to *Althea rosea* (hollyhock), which is greener (i.e. less hairy), hardier, and taller, and flowers in a variety of colours. Hollyhock grows wild anywhere in Greece, as well as in gardens, and has almost the same therapeutic properties as marshmallow.

32. Mistletoe
Birdlime mistletoe

Greek names: Ixós, elaténio, ghi, miliás, méla, melás
Latin name: *Viscum album*

Description: This parasitic plant, well-known as a Christmas decoration, grows in several common trees but especially the fir, its roots taking nourishment from the wood of the host. The sparse leaves, set terminally in striking opposite pairs, are long, narrow and fleshy. The fruits are small white berries containing a glutinous substance much loved by birds.

Uses and preparations

— HYPERTENSION: Make an infusion with the leafy branches, preferably in wine, using 40 g of mistletoe to 1 litre wine. Allow to stand for several days, then strain. Drink 100 g of the tisane daily.

— STOMACH UPSETS: It is believed that swallowed whole like pills, the fruits are very good for the stomach generally.

Habitat: In Greece, mistletoe is most easily found where there are fir trees. Although it also grows on other trees, the plant from firs as its host is acknowledged to be the most efficacious.

Directions for gathering: Collect leaves all the year round, together with the twigs. The fruits ripen in winter.

NOTES Theophrastus, Pliny and Paracelsus considered this plant a marvellous medication in the treatment of epilepsy. The Celts, too, valued it highly, and used it for a great variety of illnesses. Their priestly Druids used to dip mistletoe branches in water, and this water was then considered a powerful medicine for every kind of sickness.

The active constituents of the plant have not yet been isolated, but may be albumins (viscotoxin), and derivatives of choline.

33. Mulberry
Black and White mulberry

Greek names: Mouriá, sikaminiá, skamniá, asprosikamniá, dountiá (N. Greece), samdoudoú (Cyprus), mavroskamniá, mourgána, xinomouriá
Latin names: *Morus alba* and *M. nigra*

Description: These are two very similar species of small tree with oval to heart-shaped leaves, rough above for *M. nigra* (which has dark purplish-red fruits), but smooth for *M. alba* (whitish fruit). The fruits resemble elongated raspberries or blackberries.

Uses and preparations
— WEAKNESS and GENERAL DEBILITY: Bring to the boil 200 g fresh or dried mulberry bark, 50 g quinine, 100 g sugar and 400 g wine. Of this liquid, one wineglassful should be taken regularly for a while at noon before meals.
— MOUTH ULCERS, IRRITATION of the MUCOUS MEMBRANES INSIDE THE MOUTH: Make a syrup by boiling fresh fruits in water and take one spoonful three times a day, retaining it in the mouth for a while before swallowing. This rather viscous syrup is known in Greece as mulberry honey.

Habitat: A common tree everywhere in Greece, both in its wild form and cultivated in gardens, parks and orchards.

Directions for gathering: Mulberry bark may be gathered any time of the year; the fruits ripen early in the summer.

NOTES The black-berried mulberry was known in ancient times as *sikaminos* (Theophrastus) and *moréa* (Dioscurides). The white-fruited species first came to Greece in Byzantine times, together with the first silkworms from China, which feed almost exclusively on mulberry leaves.

34. Mullein

Aaron's rod, Blanket herb, Cow's lungwort, Lady's foxglove

Greek names: Splónos, phlómos, glóssa, melissaroú, melíssandros, aspríonas, aspiriónas (Mani), zohadovótano (Thrace), kolliandroúdia

Latin name: *Verbascum* sp.

Description: These biennial plants form a basal rosette of leaves in the first year, and in the second year a flower stem of 1-2 m or more in height. All parts of the plants of this genus are extremely hairy. The flower stem, which may be branched, has leaves growing up part of its length, and the yellow, five-petalled flowers (1.5-3 cm across) are borne in the upper section in more or less dense spike formation.

Uses and preparations

— DIAORRHEA, DYSENTERY: Make a tisane with 20-30 g of dried leaves to 1 litre of water, and drink of this frequently.

— CATARRH: Make a decoction from 5-10 dried flowers per glassful of water, let stand, drain well and drink as a tea.

— NEURALGIA, GASTRITIS, RHEUMATIC PAINS, TRACHEITIS (inflammation of the trachea): Drink a tisane made from preferably fresh pieces of the plant (a handful per small saucepan), gathered shortly before flowering.

Habitat: Most of the mulleins grow in mountainous, rocky areas, though some are occasionally found at lower elevations.

Directions for gathering: Leaves and flower shoots are collected in spring shortly before the flowers open, the flowers themselves (those of the larger-flowered species are more potent) in spring and summer. They must be dried quickly in the open air in the shade, because slow drying discolours them and makes them lose their therapeutic value.

NOTES All species of mullein contain abundant mucilage,

volatile oil, sugar, xanthophyll and saponins. Mulleins are poisonous to livestock and are avoided by them.

35. Nettle
Stinging nettle

Greek names: Tsouknída, tsiknída, tsoúkna, skníthra
Latin name: *Urtica dioica*

Description: A perennial plant with erect fibrous stems up to 1 m high, and with rhizome roots sending out subterranean shoots. The leaves are pointed ovals, with a deeply serrated edge. The small, greenish flowers grow in semi-drooping tassels from the leaf axils. Both stems and leaves are densely covered in hairs which, except in very young plants, cause intense itching and swelling when they come into contact with the skin. Other species of nettle have not dissimilar pharmaceutical properties.

Uses and preparations
— WEAKNESS and GENERAL DEBILITY, ANAEMIA: Make an infusion from one whole dried branch of the plant in a glassful of water, and drink a wineglassful of the liquid every morning. Alternatively, the young plant can be eaten raw as a salad, or boiled and eaten like spinach.

See also preparation given under DANDELION.

— ARTHRITIS: Put on gloves and hit the affected area with a stem of fresh stinging nettle to stimulate blood circulation. This will cause a burning feeling and temporary swelling, but is a very effective remedy.

— CHRONIC HEPATITIS, CHOLESTEROL, BRONCHITIS, RHEUMATISM, FAILING MILK in nursing mothers: Boil a few leaves, or three or four of the large round seeds of *U. pilulifera*, common in Greece, in a small panful of water until volume is reduced by half. Strain, and drink half a wineglassful once or twice a day.

Habitat: All over Greece on road sides, in fields, hedges and wastegrounds.

Directions for gathering: Collect entire young plants for eating raw in early spring. For drying, gather stems in spring when developing (wear gloves to avoid being stung). Dry in the shade at no more than 50° C. Rhizome roots for drying may be taken at any time, but least painfully before there is much growth above ground.

NOTES The burning toxin in the stinging hairs has little medicinal value. The active constituents of the plant are not yet understood, but it contains histamin, large quantities of chlorophyll and xanthophyll, carotin, sodium nitrate, calcium nitrate, an abundance of vitamin C, iron, glycosites and glycosin, pyritic acid, enzymes etc.

36. Onion

Greek names: Kremmídi, krommídi
Latin name: *Allium cepa*

Description: This is the bulb universally in culinary use, both raw and cooked. It is too well known to require detailed description. In above-ground growth it resembles garlic *(q. v.)*.

Uses and preparations

— LOSS OF HAIR, BALDING: Crush raw onion, draw off juice, mix 60 g of this with 15 g potassium carbonate and 240 g water. Shake well and store in a sealed bottle. Massage the scalp with this liquid daily.

— ATONY (lassitude): Eat at least one raw onion per day (onion soup may be taken as an alternative, but is less effective). There will be almost immediate improvement in the condition.

— HYPERTENSION: Onion is one of the best diuretics and lowers the blood pressure. One onion, preferably raw, should be taken each day with meals.

— ARTERIOSCLEROSIS, CIRRHOSIS of the LIVER: An onion a day, preferably taken raw, together with food.

— BEE and WASP STINGS: After removing the sting if necessary, put on a poultice of crushed raw onion, or even just a slice of raw onion, letting the juice soak into the skin.

— HAEMORRHOIDS: Fry an onion in pork fat and when it has cooled down, place on the affected area and leave for as long as possible.

— BURNS: Apply a poultice of crushed onion mixed with a little salt, or even just a slice of raw onion lightly salted.

Habitat: Widespread in fields and gardens, but most easily obtained from greengrocers.

Directions for gathering: Mature specimens from the shops all

the year round, or young plants in spring, sold as spring-onions. Almost always used fresh.

NOTES Onion contains saccaroses, calcium phosphate, calcium nitrate, calcium acetate, fluorine, iodine, vitamins A, B and C, and volatile oil.

Onion originated in Central Asia, but has been cultivated in Greece since the time of Homer. It was also known to the Chaldeans and the ancient Egyptians. For the latter, it seems to have had religious significance, as it is the most frequently depicted plant in the tombs of the Pharaohs. Theophrastus describes it in minute detail, and also gives its many variant species.

37. Pear

Greek names: Agriahladiá, gortsiá
Latin name: *Pyrus communis*, s. sp. *pyraster*

Description: This is a deciduous tree very similar to the cultivated pear, but with smaller almost round leaves and small, tart fruit. The five-petalled flowers are white and grow in massed bunches in spring.

Uses and preparations

— ENTEROCOLITIS: Take a little of the root, 60 g of fishglue, 1 litre wine and half a litre water. Boil and reduce to three-quarters of the original amount. Use the resulting liquid for making coffee and drink small amounts of this frequently for two days.

— FREQUENT MENSTRUATION: Make a decoction of roots in wine, and use the liquid in place of water when making coffee. Drink this repeatedly, not adding any sugar.

Habitat: On high mountainous ground in central and northern Greece.

Directions for gathering: Collect the root at any time of the year, though it is most potent taken in summer when the tree is fully active.

NOTES Wild pear is the forebear of the cultivated fruit tree. A related species is *pyrus amygdaliformis* (almond-shaped pear), which is found in southern Greece and the Peloponnese and may have the same medicinal properties.

38. Pellitory-of-the-wall

Greek names: Perdikáki, perdikoúli, anemolíti, kolissóhor-
to, anemóhorto, parthenoúdi

Latin name: *Parietaria officinalis*

Description: A more or less erect perennial, not very much branched, from 30-100 cm high. The leaves are slimly elliptical, pointed at both ends, smooth above and clingingly hairy beneath. Very small, greenish flowers grow in the leaf axils all the way up, around, and close to the stem. They turn red as they ripen into seeds. There are several related species with the same common Greek names (in English there are the subspecies Mind-your-own-business, and Mother-of-thousands), all of which have similar physical characteristics.

Uses and preparations

— NEPHRITIS, CYSTITIS: Make an infusion with 10-20 g of the plant to 1 litre of water, and drink the tisane repeatedly.

— INFLAMMATION of the SKIN: Boil pieces of the stem with leaves and flowers in a little water for a short while, and cool. When lukewarm, apply them to the inflamed area as a poultice. Leave for a considerable time.

Habitat: An extremely common species on waste grounds, vacant lots, old walls etc.

Directions for gathering: Collect in spring while in flower.

NOTES This appears to be Dioscurides' *elzíni* or *parthénio*. It contains potassium nitrate, sulphur, and a glutinous substance.

39. Plantain

Great plantain, Ripplegrass, Waybread, Ribwort, Long plantain, Snake plantain, *et al.*

Greek names: Pentanevro, perdikopátima, kiparrisóhorto, psilóhorto (Corfu), psaráki (Máni), piknóhorto (Santoríni)

Latin name: *Plantago* (all species)

Description: This is a large genus of plants , all the members of which have certain characteristics in common.The leaves, varying from narrow lance-shaped to broad elliptical, and always forming a basal rosette, are in all species strongly marked with five parallel nerves running their full length.The tiny flowers are borne on long, generally smooth stalks, and concentrated at the top of the flower stem in spikes of varying lengths.

Uses and preparations

— WOUNDS and SORES: Lightly crush dried or fresh plantain leaves by rubbing them in the palm of the hand. Apply to the affected area and tie up with gauze or cloth to stop bleeding and promote healing.

— DIARRHOEA: Make a decoction with two tablespoonsful of dried leaves to 1 litre of water, boiling for 3 minutes. Drink the liquid when it has cooled a little. Alternatively, as a mild purgative for slight diarrhoea, allow one to three teaspoonsful of ripe seeds to swell for two hours in a tumblerful of water and then swallow them whole.

Habitat: All species of plantain are quite common in Greece, and at least one can be found in every area.

Directions for gathering: Collect leaves almost all the year round. Seeds ripen in summer. There are both annual and perennial species of plantain. It is generally the dried (rarely the fresh) leaves that are used.

NOTES Plantain contains mucilage and the glycoside aucubin, and probably also antibacterial or bacteria-inhibiting substances.

The medicinal properties of the genus have been acknowledged since the time of Theophrastus and Dioscurides, who mention it under the common names of *arnóglosson* (lamb's tonque), *vouprístis*, *koronópous*, *kínops*, *órtyx* and *stelléphouros*.

40. Parsley

Greek names: Maïndanós, makedonísi, petrosélino (Corfu), persémolo (Corfu), mirodiá, kondouméndo
Latin name: *Petroselinum sativum*

Description: Both the wild and the cultivated plant form a basal rosette of leaves in the first year, and in the second year they throw up a flower stalk as much as 80 cm high. The leaves — shiny, or in the cultivated form also crimped *(P. crispum)* — are much segmented and further and further subdivided (triangularly two to three times pinnate). The small white or greenish-yellow flowers are borne in loose, umbrella-like structures (umbels) at the top of the stem and its side-branches.

Uses and preparations

— DROPSY, KIDNEY STONES, SAND in the KIDNEYS: Make an infusion in half a litre of water of 1 tablespoonful of finely chopped fresh or dried leaves, or 1 teaspoonful of finely chopped root, or one to two knife-points of crushed green fruits, and drink a waterglassful of the liquid morning and night for one week.

— HYPERTENSION: Make an infusion with fresh or dried parsley leaves and drink of the tisane frequently.

— SEPTIC OPTHALMITIS, BREAST ABSCESS (in women): Make a poultice with boiled parsley leaves, and while still lukewarm apply to the affected area.

Warning: Large doses must be avoided, especially by pregnant women, because of the effect of parsley on the blood flow.

Habitat: Wild in rocky locations in northern Greece; in cultivated form available at greengrocers everywhere.

Directions for gathering: Use leaves and roots, fresh and dried. Collect for drying at any time in late spring or in summer.

NOTES Parsley is mentioned by Dioscurides under the name of *petrosélino*. Theophrastus speaks about a plant called *oreiosélino*, which is believed to be the same. In ancient times the plant was used only medicinally, today it is mostly known as a kitchen flavouring.

Parsley contains volatile oil, fatty substances, pectin, tannin, cobalt, iron, iodine, magnesium phosphorus, sodium, sulphur, apiol, chloride, manganese and potassium. The root has additionally large quantities of starch.

41. Pomegranate

Greek names: Rodiá, roïdiá, roviá (Cyprus)
Latin name: *Punica granatum*

Description: A large deciduous spiny shrub with small, oval, shiny and leathery leaves. The fleshy bright red flowers are bellshaped and have a mass of fine yellow stamens. The red calyx at the bell top gradually evolves into the fruit. Pomegranates are the size of oranges, round, with a bumpily leathery skin with salmon-red blushes or streaks, enclosing hundreds of tiny seeds, each encased in a round, pink, juicy fruit-sack. It is these individual seed-'pearls' that are eaten, but there are also sour, inedible varieties of pomegranate.

Uses and preparations
— TAPEWORM (intestinal): Take 50 g finely cut bark of the root, and leave to soak for 24 hours in two tumblersful of water. Bring very slowly to boiling point, and then boil rapidly until only half the liquid remains. This is drunk in two or three doses over 24 hours. Since the liquid is extremely bitter, essence of mint or a little honey may be added. After the medicine has taken effect, the patient should be given a cathartic.
— AMOEBIC INTESTINAL DISORDERS: Drink a decoction made with the peal of one whole fruit boiled up with two tumblersful of water.

Habitat: Grows all over Greece, both wild and in cultivated form.

Directions for gathering: The root may be collected at any time of the year, but best of all in autumn. The fruits ripen in late summer.

NOTES Homer mentions pomegranate as one of the plants which were grown in his time, and he tells us that King Alkinoos of the Phaeacians systematically cultivated this beautiful shrub. Theophrastus, much later, writes about many variant species, including one the edible seed-'pearls' of which mercifully contained no pips. In Pliny the pomegranate goes under the

name of *malum punicum* and he says it was brought to Europe from Carthage, though this does not in fact seem to have been the case. The ancient Greeks called the plant *riá* or *róa*.

42. Purple Loosestrife
Greek names: Líthro, salikária
Latin name: *Lythrum salicaria*

Description: This is an erect, hairy perennial, the straight stems of which grow up to 1.50 tall and, except very early in the year, are woody at the base. Lance-shaped leaves grow in opposite pairs, half-joined where they spring from the stem. The flowers are arranged in layers of dense whorls one above the other on the upper part of the stem, and are varying shades of bright rose-purple.

Uses and preparations
— DIARRHOEA, MICROBIC DYSENTERY, DISORDERS of the DIGESTIVE SYSTEM: Make an infusion with 5-10 dried or fresh flowers to a glassful of water, and drink the liquid as tea.

— VARICOSE ULCERS, ECZEMA, ITCHING: Put 5-10 fresh or dried flowers into a glass of pure alcohol, seal the container to prevent evaporation, and leave for ten days. After straining, use as a liniment.

— WOUNDS and SORES, INTERNAL HAEMORRHAGES: Bruise fresh clean leaves of loosestrife and apply to the affected area externally.

Habitat: In all of Greece, close to streams, ditches and rivers, and in damp locations generally.

Directions for gathering: Collect stems with leaves and flowers in summer while blossoming.

43. Rosemary

Romero

Greek names: Dendrolívano, Iasmarí (Cyprus)
Latin name: *Rosmarinus officinalis*

Description: A rather stiffly erect evergreen shrub, the branches of which are woody at the base and pliantly tender towards the tip. The leaves are needle-shaped (linear), soft, and a greyish green on the underside. The flowers grow in the leaf axils towards the ends of the shoots. The corolla is two-lipped (see photo), and skyblue in colour. All parts of the plant give off a very pleasing aroma when crushed.

Uses and preparations

— CARDIAC LASSITUDE, HEART IRREGULARITY: Put a few tender fresh pieces from the ends of the shoots, or dried rosemary, into a bottle of wine and leave to stand for several days. Drink one wineglassful per day.

— WOUNDS and SORES: Put powder of crushed dried leaves on the wound to disinfect and promote healing.

— LOSS OF HAIR, BALDING: Soak a few branches of rosemary, chopped roots of nettles *(q.v.)* and roots of burdock *(q.v.)* in a bottle of pure alcohol. Use as a liniment to massage the balding part.

— DYSENTERY: Boil a handful of chopped, dried rosemary root in two tumblersful of wine until only one-third of the volume remains. Drink the liquor once or twice a day.

— CHRONIC DYSPEPSIA, CHRONIC PULMONARY CATARRH: Make an infusion with 10-30 g of flowering branch-tops in water, and drink the tisane once or twice a day.

— RHEUMATISM, MIGRAINE: Gently massage the affected parts with the above tisane as a liniment.

Habitat: Frequently planted in parks and gardens. Widespread also in the wild form, especially on the flanks of Mt Ritsónas near Halkida.

Directions for gathering: May be collected throughout the year,

but most usefully in spring when it flowers. Generally used dried, also for culinary purposes.

NOTES This is probably the plant referred to by Dioscurides in the *Fourth Libanoti* under the name of *rosmarinum*.
   Pharmaceutical use includes the leaves *(folia rosmarini)*, the tender branch-tops *(herba rosmarini)*, as well as the scented oil *(oleum rosmarini)*. The plant contains volatile oil and tannin.

44. Sage

Greek names: Phaskómilo, alisphakiá, aliphaskiá
Latin name: *Salvia officinalis*

Description: A shrubby perennial plant with numerous branches up to 50 cm high, woody at the base, the upper part of the square stems tender and covered with felted hair. The leaves are elongated and pointed ovals, hairy and greyish-green. The two-lipped flowers — light to violet blue — appear at the end of spring, arranged all closely together in successive whorls at the top of the stems.

Uses and preparations

— ATONY of (sluggish) STOMACH, WEAKNESS and GENERAL DEBILITY, MENSTRUAL IRREGULARITIES, WEAK MEMORY: Put one or two tablespoonsful of finely chopped fresh or dried leaves into 1 litre of water, raise to the boil and allow to stand. Drink as a tea and/or in place of plain water.

— LOSS OF HAIR, BALDING: Frequently massage the scalp with the above tisane. Repeat regularly over a considerable period.

— FLACCID SKIN (facial): Boil tender shoots of sage in water. Remove from heat. Hold face over the pot for ten minutes or so, covering the head and the pot with a towel to prevent the steam from escaping. Alternatively, dip a cloth into the liquor when this has cooled sufficiently and use as a compress.

— THROAT INFLAMMATION, INFLAMED GUMS: Use first recipe given above and employ the tisane as a gargle or a mouthwash.

— COLDS: Make sage tea (first recipe given above) and drink it hot two or three times a day.

— EXCESSIVE PERSPIRATION, NIGHT SWEATS: Make an infusion with sage leaves (see first recipe given above) and store the liquor in a bottle. Drink one waterglassful at night before retiring. Even better results are obtained if, instead of the infusion, 30 drops of juice from the fresh plant are taken nightly.

Warning: Sage must not be taken by people with haematuria (blood in the urine) or those with high blood pressure.

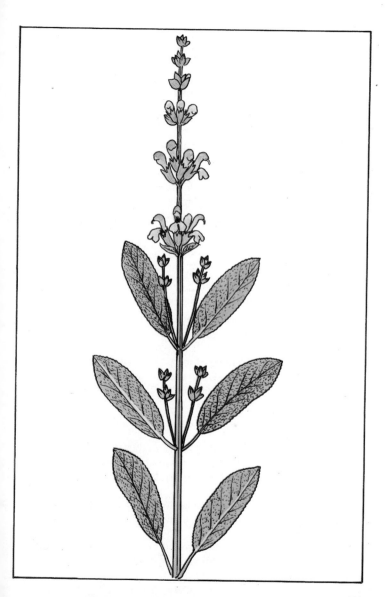

Habitat: Sage grows in dry rocky places in full sun at low altitudes in southern Greece, the Peloponnese and on the islands.

Directions for gathering: Collect leaves and tender shoots in spring before flowering and again in September-October. Dry in the shade at less than 35° C. Fresh leaves are also used as a flavouring in meat and fish dishes, soups etc.

NOTES Sage contains tannin, tannosetonin, and strong volatile oil.

Dioscurides mentions it under the name of *eleliphaskos*. Pharmaceutically it is known as *herba salviae,* and the French call it Greek tea *(thé de grèce).* The Arabs value it as a panacea for all illnesses. They have a saying: "He still had sage in his yard and yet he died?"

45. Stone fern
Scaly spleenwood

Greek names: Skorpídi, Chryssóhorto
Latin name: *Ceterach officinarum*

Description: A small species of fern, the leaves of which do not exceed 15 cm in length. They are lance-shaped and deeply indented on both sides, smooth above, but covered in dense blond hairs on the underside.

Uses and preparation
— KIDNEY STONES, COMPLAINTS of the URINARY SYSTEM: Make an infusion with the dried leaves or the whole plant, and drink at least one glassful of the liquid per day.

Habitat: On hills and mountains, in shady places among the rocks, and in similar situations anywhere in Greece.

Directions for gathering: May be gathered throughout the year. Take the whole plant, or preferably cut only the growth above the ground. Dry and store.

46. Shepherd's purse

Greek names: Agriokardamoúda, tzourkás
Latin name: *Capsella bursa-pastoris*

Description: This annual forms a basal rosette of downy leaves which are deeply toothed into lobes, which themselves have toothed edges and lie flat against the ground. From the centre of this rosette grows a 10-50 cm high flower stem. The flowers are borne many of them close together at the top: later the stem lengthens, and when the seeds have developed, they are much more widely spaced. The flowers are very small, white, cruciform in shape, and each has its own small stalk. This too grows longer as the seed capsule develops into its characteristic triangular to heartshaped outline.

Uses and preparations

— HYPERTENSION: Make an infusion of a litre of cold water to 1-2 tablespoonsful of the fresh or died plant, and drink one small glass of the liquid per day.

— INTERNAL HAEMORRHAGES (especially for profuse menstruation, when treatment should start 8 days before onset): Make an infusion as given above, and drink at least two wineglassesful a day.

Habitat: On flat land anywhere, in cultivated as well as fallow farmland.

Directions for gathering: Collect in spring to early summer while flowering. Dry in the shade. Shepherd's purse can be sown in the garden in autumn.

NOTES Shepherd's purse is probably the *thláspi* of Dioscurides. It contains choline and other amines, as well as boracic acid etc.

47. Spearmint
Garden mint

Greek names: Diósmos, diósmi, aghiasmós (Corfu), ménda
Latin name: *Mentha viridis*

Description: A plant with subterranean spreading shoots, erect square stems, and oval leaves. The very small flowers are pinkish-lilac in colour, growing in closely-packed blunt spikes at the tips of the stems. All parts of the plant give off a strong aromatic scent.

Uses and preparations

— COLIC, STOMACH CRAMPS, VOMITING: Make an infusion with one tablespoonful of dried spearmint to half a litre of water. Strain, add a little honey and aniseed essence. Take one spoonful repeatedly at frequent intervals.

— ABSCESSES: Place powder from dried crushed leaves on the affected area and tie up gently.

See also Elder for INFLUENZA.

Habitat: Spearmint is found growing wild in northern Greece, and cultivated all over the country.

Directions for gathering: May be collected all the year round and dried, or can be grown in a flower pot to be available fresh at all times.

NOTES It is likely that this is the species mentioned by Theophrastus as *idíosmos* or *mínthi,* and by Dioscurides as *idíosmon of the day.*

Spearmint contains volatile oil, carvone, and traces of tannin, and stimulates gastric secretion.

48. Speedwell

Common speedwell, Bird's eye

Greek name: Veroníki
Latin name: *Veronica officinalis*

Description: Small perennial creeping plant with erect flowering stems 10-40 cm high. The opposite-placed leaves are oval oblongs, hairy, and have finely toothed edges. The four-petalled flowers are a delicate light blue, tinged faintly with purple, and grow in loose spikes at the tip of the stems.

Uses and preparations

— ATONY (lassitude) of the STOMACH, STOMACH CRAMPS, BRONCHIAL CATARRH: Make a decoction of the dried flowering plant by boiling two tablespoonsful in half a litre of water for 20 minutes, and drink while still warm.

— SKIN ERUPTIONS, SPOTS and PIMPLES, SLOW-HEALING WOUNDS: Use the decoction given above and apply externally as a lotion or as compresses.

— INFLAMED EYES: Boil the tips of the stems complete with flowers in a minimum of water and use a poultice by soaking pieces of cottonwool in the liquid and spreading it over the lids.

Habitat: In highland forests in northern Greece only.

Directions for gathering: Collect in summer during its flowering season. Pick only the upper parts of the stems with the flower spikes.

NOTES Speedwell contains organic acids, lactic acid, acetic acid, tartaric acid, mannitic acid, traces of volatile oil etc.

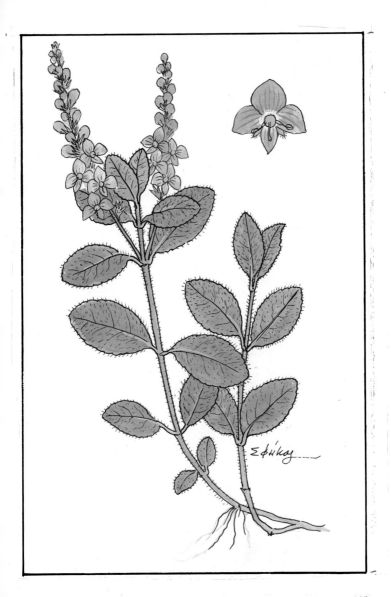

Σφήκας

49. Strawberry

Wild strawberry

Greek names: Phráoula, agriophráoula, hamokéraso
Latin name: *Fragaria vesca*

Description: Like its much larger cultivated relative, wild strawberry sends out long runners above ground (stolons) which root themselves at the tip and form rosettes of leaves. Each of the stalked leaves is divided into three equal sections joined at the centre (trifoliate). They are coarsely toothed and hairy on the underside. The five-petalled white flowers develop into the edible fruits with a very distinctive flavour; they resemble the cultivated strawberry, but are only about 1 cm in size.

Uses and preparations

— DEFICIENT BLOOD CIRCULATION, CLOTTED BLOOD VESSELS: Boil the fruits of the plant, i.e. the strawberries, and drink the tisane.

— DIARRHOEA: Drink an infusion made with 3-5 dried leaves per two tumblersful of water.

— KIDNEY HAEMORRHAGE: Take half a litre of dark wine, 100 g dried strawberry leaves, 10 g mastica, 10 g fish glue, bring to the boil, and allow to stand. Drink two cupsful of this daily.

Habitat: In woodland locations in the central and northern Greek highlands, often among ferns.

Directions for gathering: Collect leaves at any time in summer, and the fruits in June.

NOTES Wild strawberry fruits contain vitamin C, iron, calcium and phosphorus. The cultivated varieties may have the same medicinal properties.

50. Valerian
Setwall

Greek names: Valeriána, agriosamboúkos
Latin name: *Valeriana officinalis*

Description: A perennial plant with short, 2-cm thick rhizome roots which send out subterranean runners from the second year onwards and produce new shoots above ground in spring, often 1 m tall or more. The leaves are divided into several narrow, feather-like sections (pinnate). The tiny pink or white flowers grow in round-topped clusters at the branched ends of the shoots. The characteristic which distinguishes this species from other valerians is the deep groove marks (striations) up the round stems. The dried root has a peculiar strong smell.

Uses and preparations

— OBESITY: To support the prescribed dietary regimen, make an infusion with 30-40 g of dried leaves per 1 litre of water, and drink instead of tea. (Valerian is a depressant acting on the central nervous system.)

— EPILEPSY, HYSTERIA, NERVOUS SPASMS: Boil 10 g of dried rhizome root in 1 litre of water for a minute or two, and drink the decoction in place of tea.

— INSOMNIA (mild): Soak a spoonful of finely chopped rhizome roots in a glassful of cold water and leave to stand for 24 hours. Drink at night before retiring.

Habitat: Valerian is rather rare in Greece, and is to be sparsely found only in the north, in damp meadow locations in the mountains.

Directions for gathering: Collect rhizomes and leaves in summer while plant is flowering, and dry.

NOTES Valerian is also cultivated in gardens and is very popular with cats — hence its French name *herb aux chats.*
Its active principles are the recently discovered valepotriates,

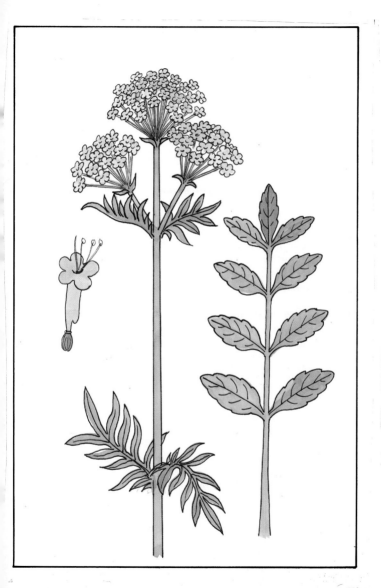

a volatile oil, and a spasmolytic substance which depresses the central nervous system.

51. Vervain

Holy herb, Simplers' joy

Greek names: Stavrovótano, gorgóyianni, stavróhorto, splinóhorto, spiróhorto
Latin name: *Verbena officinalis*

Description: This stiff, erect, square-stemmed plant is a perennial with hairy leaves, the lower ones deeply segmented into toothed lobes, and the upper ones whole and tooth-edged. Much-branching slender stems carry very small, light blue or mauve flowers, at first in dense clusters but soon elongating into slender spikes.

Uses and preparations:

— SEPTIC WOUNDS: Boil dried leaves briefly in a little water and apply as a poultice. Fresh leaves may be used instead, which are then merely bruised by rubbing them between the hands before applying them to the wound.

— FAILING MILK in nursing mothers, FEVER, STOMACH UPSETS: Make a tisane from two or three dried branches with leaves and flowers per glassful of water, and drink regularly until recovery is effected.

Habitat: Very common in waste grounds and by road sides.

Directions for gathering: Collect shoots for drying in spring and summer when in full flower.

NOTES This is thought to be the species that Dioscurides refers to as the "sacred herb" or *peristereón ýptios.* For the Romans, who called it *vervinacum,* as for the Gauls also, it had divine attributes and was used in religious ceremonies and rites.

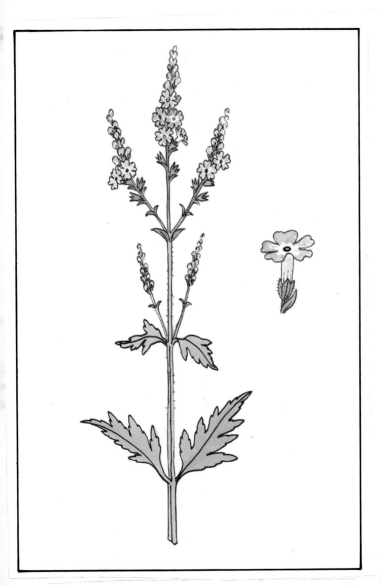

52. Violet

Blue violet, Sweet violet

Greek names: Menexés, vióla, violétta, yioúlia (Ionian islands), ítso, manousáki

Latin name: *Viola odorata*

Description: A low perennial with heart- or kidney-shaped leaves on long stems, their edges toothed, and all growing from the head of the central tap root. The branched rhizome root sends off surface runners which root at the ends. The violet-coloured flowers grow on slim stalks from the centre of the plant, and have five petals, the lowest of which has a short blunt spur at the back.

Uses and preparations

— CATARRH, BRONCHITIS, INFLAMMATION of the LUNGS or KIDNEYS: Boil one or two tablespoonsful of the finely chopped dried plant in half a litre of water and drink the tisane in the place of tea.

— CANCER of the SKIN: It is believed (but not yet proven) that eating fresh violet leaves over a long period of time will cure skin cancer.

Habitat: Violet grows wild in the Greek highland forests, but is more easily obtained from gardens, where it is often grown for its scent.

Directions for gathering: All of the plant is used. In Greece it flowers during the winter. Dry in the shade. (Dog violet, *V. canina*, which does not grow in Greece, has almost the same medical properties.)

NOTES Blue violet was known in ancient times under the name of *íon.*

The plant contains saponins and derivatives of salicylic acids, and the root also has violan, an acrid and styptic essence.

53. Walnut

Greek name: Karidiá
Latin name: *Juglans regia*

Description: This large deciduous tree provides the well-known walnuts. Its leaves are large and shiny, divided into many leaflets on both sides of a central rib (pinnate). The bark of the trunk is grey and smooth, becoming fissured in older specimens.

Uses and preparations

— CORNS and BUNIONS: Crush fresh bark and apply as a poultice.

— LOSS OF HAIR, BALDING: Make a decoction with fresh walnut leaves and frequently wash the hair with this liquid.

— SHINGLES, WARTS: Apply juice from crushed fresh walnut leaves, or from the green nut case.

— WOUNDS: Apply a poultice made from boiled leaves.

— SUGAR DIABETES, ARTHRITIS: Drink an infusion of fresh walnut leaves.

Habitat: Self-propagating in the Greek forests of the north, but also cultivated in many highland villages and in city parks.

Directions for gathering: Leaves can be collected all the year round, but are at their most potent in early summer. They must be dried quickly in the shade, because slow drying turns them black and spoils their effectiveness. The green nut-cases are ready in late summer and are removed from the fruit for drying.

NOTES Walnut leaves contain tannin, a little volatile oil, and the bitter essence juglone. The bark contains tannic substances, and the green nut-casing is rich in vitamin C.

54. Wormwood

Absinthe

Greek names: Apsithiá, agriapsithiá (Crete), pélino (Thessaly), pisidiá (Crete), melitíni (Cephalonia), apsiphiá

Latin name: *Artemisia absinthium*

Description: A shrubby, much-branched perennial plant with woody root stock, marked scent, and bitter taste. Flowering shoots are up to 1 m tall. The leaves are deeply divided into five or more sections, each further subdivided. The undersides of the leaves and shoots are densely covered in a silvery hairy down, giving the whole plant a gray look. The flowers grow up the length of the shoots as tiny, yellowish-green florets.

Uses and preparations

— DROPSY: Pound dried wormwood flowers and shoots to powder and make a cold infusion of this in 1 litre of water (do not boil). Drink at least a litre of this per day.

— TAPEWORM (intestinal): Add 10-30 g of dried wormwood pounded to powder to 1 litre of white wine, and drink one wineglassful of this before meals.

— URINE RETENTION, KIDNEY STONES, AMENORRHEA (suppression of menstrual flow), STOMACH UPSETS, FEVER, as a DIURETIC: Make a cold infusion with one or two teaspoonsful of the plant in 1 litre of water. Take one cupful two or three times a day.

See also Balm for HEART PAINS.

Warning: Wormwood should only be taken with caution during pregnancy. In general, excessive doses may produce vertigo, cramps, and even mental disturbance.

Habitat: Dry, rocky locations in the Greek highlands.

Direction for gathering: Collect upper shoots in summer while flowering, and dry in the shade.

NOTES This is thought to be the plant mentioned by Dioscurides

as *absinthion*, from which absinth wine was made in Thrace and Propontida, which was used as a medication for a variety of illnesses. It is the volatile oil contained in the plant which is poisonous in large quantities, and which was used in antiquity in the making of the notorious drink *aphenti*. This drink was eventually prohibited in many countries because it had become something of a social scourge, being addictive.

55. Yarrow
Milfoil, Nosebleed, Thousandleaf

Greek names: Hilióphyllo, agriapsithiá, semesándo
Latin name: *Achillea millefolium*

Description: Erect perennial plant up to 80 cm high, with rhizome roots and hairy stems, branched in the upper part and terminating in flat-topped, compound flower clusters. The leaves are lanceolate in outline, but much segmented into very many fine leaflets on either side of a central rib (twice pinnate) — hence "Thousandleaf". The small flowers have five blunt white petals, occasionally pink, around a yellow centre. The species is rather variable.

Uses and preparations
— SEPTIC WOUNDS, WOUNDS and BRUISES: Lightly crush fresh leaves and apply as a poultice. Cover, and leave on as long as possible.
— MENSTRUAL HAEMORRHAGE, INTERNAL HAEMORRHAGES, SUGAR DIABETES (in the early stages), RHEUMATISM, ARTHRITIS: Soak two or three tablespoonsful of dried flowering stems per 1 litre cold water, and allow to stand. Drink this regularly. Alternatively, make a hot infusion.
— EARACHE: Pour a few drops of the almost cold infusion into the ear.
See also Dandelion for GENERAL FATIGUE of the ORGANISM.

Habitat: Dry roadside locations as well as highland pastures in nearly all of mainland Greece.

Directions for gathering: Collect flowering stems in summer when blooming. Dry in the shade at less than 40° C.

NOTES Yarrow flowers *(flores millefolii)* as well as the whole plant *(herba millefolii)* have been used pharmaceutically since ancient times.
   The active constituents are bitter principles and volatile oil, making the plant anti-inflammatory and anti-spasmodic.

INDEX

Plants with ENGLISH NAMES are arranged alphabetically in the text, unless otherwise stated.
Greek names (only the most common is given for each plant, and the accented syllable is marked), and *Latin* names are followed by the number of the plant as listed under its English name.

BIBLIOGRAPHY

Votanikón kai Phytologikón Lexikón	D. Kavvádas
Érevna epi ton Pharmakeftikón Phytón	
tis Harádras tou Víkou	K. Ganiátsas
Sýnchronos Plíris Therapeftikí me ta Vótana	I. Zaharópoulos
Gymnásios o Lavriótis kai 304 Syntagaí tou	I. Primikidys

For the English edition of this book, Prof. Hans Flück's *Medicinal Plants*, (transl. Prof. J.M. Rowson), publ. Foulsham a Co., was also consulted.